DUAL DIAGNOSIS:
FACING THE CHALLENGE

The Care of People with a Dual Diagnosis of
Mental Illness and Substance Misuse

Written by

Peter Rorstad and Dr. Ken Checinski
(Main Contributors)
with
Oliver McGeachy and Mike Ward
(Editors)

Preface by Sue Dimond

Published by
Wynne Howard Publishing

Published by
Wynne Howard Publishing
27 Addison Road
Guildford
GU1 3QQ
Great Britain

First Published June 1996

British Library Cataloguing in Publication Data. A catalogue record card for
this book is available from the British Library.

Copyright 1996
Wynne Howard Publishing
ISBN 0 9525571 5 0

CONTENTS

Preface by Sue Dimond

ABOUT THE AUTHORS

Dr. Ken Checinski is a Consultant Psychiatrist in Addictive Behaviour working for the Epsom Community Drug and Alcohol Team and Greenbank Substance Misuse Recovery Centre in Surrey. He is particularly interested in the care of people with dual diagnosis and has carried out research into people with complex needs. He is academic advisor in the Training Unit at St George's Hospital Medical School, London, which runs a number of courses in addictive behaviour as well as an M.Sc.

Peter Rorstad is a freelance consultant in the health and social care field. He trained as a probation officer but spent many years establishing the North East Council on Addictions. He has recently undertaken a significant piece of research into the problem of dual diagnosis.

Oliver McGeachy is a journalist and publisher, but he has been involved with the substance misuse field since 1989. He is active in developing service user involvement and is a member of the Government's National Users and Carers Group. In his current role with English Churches Housing, he has also been instrumental in establishing specialist support services in the south east.

Mike Ward has worked in the alcohol and drugs field since leaving the University of Kent in 1980. He is currently Assistant Commissioning Manager (Alcohol and Drug Services) for Surrey Social Services.

FURTHER TRAINING

The publishers are able to provide tailor made training courses for those interested in exploring the issue of dual diagnosis. If you would like to arrange such training please write to the publishers at the address on the previous page.

"Compared with either mentally ill or chemically dependent patients, dually diagnosed patients demonstrate increased rates of hospitalisation, utilisation of acute services, housing instability and homelessness, violent and criminal behaviour....Poor medication compliance and poor response to traditional substance abuse treatment have also been associated with having dual disorders. Despite, and perhaps because of, the severe effects of co-morbidity, dually diagnosed patients are often excluded from treatment settings."

Osher and Kofoed 1989

PREFACE

This book provides an excellent introduction to, and overview of, the current situation in the UK facing those people who are trying to access help for both a mental health problem and an alcohol or drug disorder, i.e. *a dual diagnosis*.

The authors argue that, in the first instance, the term "dual diagnosis" should be seen as an expedient tool for focusing our minds on the relationship between resources for those with mental health problems, and resources for those with substance misuse problems. The process of focusing on dual diagnosis will act as an indicator of how all services can be improved for this group.

The rationale for separating mental health from substance misuse is well-known and has had general consensus. It has been effective in destigmatising these twin "Cinderella services" and has been helpful in enabling a growth of resources, particularly in the substance misuse field. However, somewhere along the way services have lost a clear vision of how mental health or mental illness and addiction can and should interact.

This book highlights starkly the dilemma of someone who experiences dual diagnosis and is shuttling between various services. Staff constraints in caring agencies are well known. Less time, job insecurity, organisational change, constant mobility of staff, increased local and national accountability have in various complex ways contributed to the concern not to take risks when faced with a "difficult dual diagnosis" client. Passing the buck is the professional side of the dual diagnosis client's experience of being shuttled back and forth between services or simply denied access.

Yet, in the book, this is balanced by highlighting that the staff of those same agencies admit to feeling, and/or being, inadequate to deal with these problems. If services are to be improved it is vital to examine with sensitivity the basis of such "inadequacy". Increasing "professionalism" in areas such as substance misuse can often produce a deskilling in otherwise competent but generic staff, and the obvious need for training must be carefully analysed.

The book emphasises the need to be mindful of the complex social and political environments within which a dually diagnosed client lives. The context is always crucial to diagnosis and treatment. For some clients their dual diagnosis will have resulted in life-threatening physical illness and harm minimisation is the best priority. For many others, especially women, there may be so many survival strategies in place as a result of abuse, violence, single-parenting or poverty that socially induced depression and substance misuse cannot be considered out of its environmental context.

This book is essential reading for all working in the community care field whose client base touches upon mental health and addiction. It is particularly aimed at service providers and purchasers. For those in the housing field it is a long awaited validation of the crucial part housing need/accommodation plays in all aspects of dual diagnosis (coincidentally, this is equally true of mental health and substance misuse as individual issues in their own rights). Many people become homeless and/or are threatened with the prospect of losing their home in the process of being dually diagnosed. At all stages, from identification through to rehabilitation, the housing circumstances and needs of the client must be prioritised.

The future of Community Care has to be holistic both in outlook and in practice. Some excellent groundwork has been laid by recent Government initiatives and it is now up to all interested parties to develop systems which embrace complex needs and diagnoses, to think and act creatively in order to integrate our varying services.

SUE DIMOND

Sue is a clinical psychologist, psychotherapist and teacher. She has run both therapeutic communities and dry houses and a project for young people leaving care. Since 1991 she has been a senior manager with English Churches Housing Group.

SECTION 1 - INTRODUCTION

Substance misuse services have long made strenuous efforts to avoid having their clients labelled as "mentally ill". It is argued that if people with alcohol or drug problems are to be attracted into specialist services, these facilities should not carry the "stigma" of the mental illness label. Specialists have also argued, with considerable reason, that substance misuse is not a mental illness and that, therefore, the two issues should be kept apart.

None of these arguments are in dispute these days. Even where social or health services continue to manage drug or alcohol services within a mental health framework, this is largely from expedience rather than a real belief that substance misuse is a psychiatric disorder. The ultimate authority for the separation of these two issues is the Mental Health Act which clearly indicates that alcohol or drug misuse is not to be considered a mental illness.

This determination to separate the two issues has probably helped many clients to feel comfortable about accessing non-stigmatised help. Yet, there is a group of clients who have been disadvantaged by these efforts, namely those with combined mental health and substance misuse problems. **The central argument of this book is that substance misusers with a mental health problem have commonly failed to access adequate treatment from either mental health or substance misuse services.**

"I was pushed around like a tennis ball. The alcohol people said that I had a mental illness and the mental illness group said I had a drink problem. Neither of them did very much for me." (Client comment).

This problem is not new. A 1978 study showed that remand prisoners with a diagnosis of both alcohol problems and mental health problems were less likely to receive help than those with mental health problems alone. (Russell 1993)

Many substance misuse services are staffed by people who have psychiatric training, for example consultant psychiatrists, nurses or social workers working in statutory teams. These staff ought to be able to address both problems. However, the evidence of this book is that this is rarely the case. Mental health services may see alcohol or drug problems as the province of specialist substance misuse services, while the latter may feel

9

that they are not set up to deal with clients who also need mental health care.

In the voluntary sector, many services openly acknowledge that they do not have such expertise. Indeed, some specialist substance misuse services make it positively difficult for dually diagnosed people to receive help by asking that clients are free of all psychotropic drugs, even those being used to control mental health conditions. Residential substance misuse services, in particular, may demand that clients are off mood-altering medication altogether, thus threatening the mental health of the dually diagnosed client. Equally, residential facilities for those with mental health problems may demand a considerable period of abstinence (three months for one client involved in the background research for this book) before admission. The dually diagnosed client faces dual problems.

A number of factors contribute to this failure to provide an adequate service:

- neither substance misuse nor mental health services feel able to address their own area of expertise due to the clouding effect of the second problem;
- the patient group is a non-vociferous and unpopular minority;
- dually diagnosed people are difficult to work with and the failure rate is high. One study showed that "mentally ill problem drinkers" had very poor outcomes from treatment. (Russell 1993)

These problems have resulted in a large group of people with a dual diagnosis being effectively disenfranchised from the right to treatment. In some ways this problem may have been exacerbated by the advent of specialist alcohol and drug services. This has allowed mental health services to refer clients out of their facilities in the hope or expectation that they will be dealt with by substance misuse specialists. In reality, they are being referred to services that do not have the capacity to deal with these needs.

On the positive side, two recent trends have meant that this problem is beginning to be recognised as an issue that needs tackling.

Firstly, the advent of Community Care and the contract culture has brought with it the requirement that local authorities and health authorities not only ensure the provision of a range of services which recognises the patterns of need within the community, but also that the outcome effectiveness of the forms of intervention purchased are demonstrated. This focus on the outcomes of care in the community has meant that the failure of services to cope with such clients is much more open to scrutiny. For example, social services department care managers will have to follow up a substance misuse client who has been asked to leave a residential facility for "inappropriate behaviour"; this could lead to the discovery that the client has a mental health problem. The health authority extra-contractual referral panel which has to consider the whole range of problems presented by a client when deciding whether to fund a client for a particular treatment, will have to balance both substance misuse and mental health needs.

The second trend has been the growing emphasis on the need to provide adequate care for Mentally Disordered Offenders (MDO's). The publication of the Reed Report (see below) and the investigations into the care of people like Christopher Clunis and John Rous, have drawn both professional and public interest. This process has uncovered, not only the large number of people with mental health problems who are coming into contact with the criminal justice system, but also the significant number of these people who also have alcohol or drug problems. For example, a study from Surrey into the number of people with mental health problems taken into police custody discovered that half of those deemed mentally disordered also had substance misuse problems (see section 3.1).

Nonetheless the core message of this book is that there is still a huge unmet need. Part of the work in this book is an investigation into the ways in which dually diagnosed people were identified and dealt with in one particular, anonymised, local authority. Its findings are clear:

- there is a problem of greater magnitude than purchasers have been aware;
- dual diagnosis is being addressed in some measure by treatment units, but not yet at an intensity or with resources appropriate to the nature and extent of the problem;
- there is little integration between services to ensure the delivery of a comprehensive treatment package to the dually diagnosed patient;
- there is an urgent need for data without which service purchasers and managers cannot hope to ensure the delivery of an appropriate pattern and range of services to dually diagnosable people.

The book also looks beyond the local situation, to look at the issue in the wider context of national and international literature on the subject. It offers some conclusions on activities to date, identifies gaps and good practices, and recommends some directions in which purchasers and providers might move to develop an effective response by recommending a strategy for ensuring more identification, assessment and treatment of dually diagnosed people.

1.2 DUAL DIAGNOSIS - A USEFUL CATEGORY?

"Dual diagnosis" is a potentially misleading, if not downright unhelpful, piece of categorisation. In many ways it is labelling of the worst kind. There are a number of powerful arguments against using this "label" in such a manner.

Why is a dual diagnosis necessarily a combined diagnosis of substance misuse and mental health problems? Could it not equally well be a diagnosis of say substance misuse problems and people with learning difficulties or of people with eating disorders and mental health problems? The only reason why dual diagnosis seems to commonly imply substance misuse and mental health problems is custom and practice.

Why just a dual diagnosis? Why not a triple or quadruple diagnosis? In reality most people do not have just an alcohol or drug problem and a mental health problem, they may well experience a constellation of problems which might more accurately be described as a multiple diagnosis. For example, one Los Angeles service is dealing with people who have AIDS/HIV, are "chemically dependent" and have mental health problems. Other people may be homeless or involved with the criminal justice system, they may have an eating disorder as well as a substance misuse and mental health problem. The list is potentially endless.

There is no such thing as "an alcohol problem" or "a drug problem" or "a mental health problem". Each one of these categories covers a myriad different sets of behaviours and consequent problems. For example, an "alcohol problem" can range from a wealthy businesswoman losing her licence in a drink/drive incident to a homeless man roaming the streets for twenty years. A "mental health problem" may range from florid psychotic behaviour to mild depression. A "drug problem" may be injecting heroin use or recreational cannabis use. Thus to combine these categories into another single category is just to perpetuate and over-extend an already strained set of labels.

These are all very logical arguments against the use of the term "dual diagnosis". The authors would have no problem agreeing with any of these criticisms. There is but one defence - **at the moment the "label" is a useful marker to draw attention to a real problem which is not being addressed.** Dual diagnosis covers a large number of varied types of behaviour and putting them into one category is almost indefensible, if it were not for the fact that health, social services, and criminal justice agencies find it easier to respond to broad categories of need rather than to thousands of individual demands for help.

It is both the hope and expectation of the authors that as awareness of this issue grows and development work begins this categorisation will be swiftly recognised as unsatisfactory and replaced by a more adequate set of definitions. Until then dual diagnosis is a crude but useful signpost to point people in the direction that must be travelled.

1.3 DEFINITIONS

This book is beset by potential problems of definition. As has been said, every one of the key terms in this debate is open to question. What is a mental health problem or a drug problem or an alcohol problem? This book is not the place to exercise these debates. Nor is it an educational text for those wishing to better understand any of these categories, however, for the sake of those with a specialism in either mental health or substance misuse alone, brief definitions only of the main categories will be given.

Mental illness - the main categories of mental illness cover:

psychotic illness - encompassing schizophrenia with its characteristic delusions, paranoia, hallucinations, jumbled thought processes and feelings of being influenced.

dementia - this is familiar to the alcohol specialist through Korsakoff's Syndrome (dementia due to the effect of alcohol on the brain). It also encompasses senile and pre-senile dementia with its characteristic failing memory and behavioural problems.

severe neurotic illness - this includes various depressive, anxiety and phobic states.

personality disorder - better known as psychopathy, this is arguably the most controversial aspect of mental illness. Indeed it is argued that personality disorder is not a mental "illness", in that it does not have an organic origin and is not treatable by medicine.

Alcohol problems - the definition of an alcohol problem is immensely complicated. There have been a number of attempts at definition. Alcoholics Anonymous define "alcoholism" as a disease characterised by loss of control over alcohol. The World Health Organisation uses the category of Alcohol Dependence Syndrome which is said to exist if someone experiences physical, psychological or social harm because of drinking. Most alcohol agencies now take a fairly pragmatic approach to the definition of alcohol problems and would suggest that if a person, or someone close to that person, was experiencing harm or problems because of his or her alcohol consumption than action should be taken.

Drug problems - the debate over the definition has taken the same path followed by alcohol problems and has reached a similar pragmatic conclusion. However, it is overlaid with a moral and legal dimension which is absent in alcohol. If a young person consumes some alcohol, it is not necessarily viewed as a problem. If a young person uses a small amount of an illegal drug, it is immediately viewed as a problem, perhaps because it is illegal, but also, some would argue, because of a moral panic about drug use.

1.4 HOW THE BOOK IS STRUCTURED

This book is based on four main sources of material. Firstly, a piece of research undertaken between November '94 and March '95 which looked at responses to dually diagnosed people in one particular health authority area in the UK. This research project focused on four key questions:

- How many people were suffering from a dual diagnosis of mental health and substance misuse problems?
- How may people were identified as experiencing these problems?
- How were they dealt with?
- With what effect?

The authors have decided not to reveal the identity of this authority or of the agencies involved in the research. It was inevitable that the study would reveal shortfalls in the response to dual diagnosis. It would, therefore, be unfair to highlight deficiencies in one area which are probably present in every other authority in the country.

The second strand is a wider review of initiatives on dual diagnosis in other parts of the country. This was undertaken at the same time as the local review and it is fair to say that it revealed little in the way of constructive responses to this problem. It does not, therefore, constitute a separate section in the book.

This work was followed by a review of the British and international literature on dual diagnosis. The British literature specifically focused on dual diagnosis is limited, but there are a variety of references to mental health problems in literature on substance misuse and references to substance misuse in literature on mental health. The American literature is much larger and reflects the greater emphasis given to dual diagnosis in that country. As one of the authors' colleagues said "I visited mental health services in Boston and the staff kept asking me what we were doing about dual diagnosis in Britain."

Finally, and just as importantly, the book draws on the practical experience of the contributors. All of the authors of the book have worked face to face with dually diagnosed clients. This experience has both informed the content and provided most of the case studies which illustrate the text.

This book is divided into eight main sections

1. The foregoing introduction covering definitions and a discussion of the usefulness of the category itself.

2. A series of case studies which highlight the various manifestations of dual diagnosis.

3. The prevalence of dual diagnosis: including an analysis of the available data on the extent of the problem.

4. A review of the literature on the nature of dual diagnosis.

5. A review of Governmental guidance which impinges on dual diagnosis in the United Kingdom.

6. A review of current responses to dual diagnosis in one part of the UK including a review of local strategies; assessment; primary worker training; specialist worker training and the dual diagnosis focus by specialist workers. This section will also focus on the major identified deficiencies in the pattern of services.

7. Recommendations for a response to dual diagnosis which is based on a model covering the four key elements of identification; assessment; treatment; and rehabilitation.

8. Useful addresses and a bibliography.

1. 5 AUTHORSHIP

The two main sections of this book - the literature review and the local research study were undertaken and drafted by Dr. Ken Checinski and Peter Rorstad. The whole volume was then edited by Mike Ward and Oliver McGeachy who take responsibility for the content and any errors.

SECTION 2 - THE CLIENTS

This section consists simply of a number of case studies of clients with both mental health and substance misuse problems, who have been encountered by the authors and their colleagues over the last two years. All are real people, although they have all been anonymised and some significant details changed in order to further protect their identities.

This section can be read as a useful grounding for what is to follow, alternatively it can be skipped entirely by those who have a sufficient familiarity with the client group. In either case, this section stands:

a) as a bank of case examples which may be used by trainers, service planners and those lobbying for change;

b) as a non-specific definition of the type of clients referred to in the subsequent text.

MIKE STANNARD - a case study

Mike was a 23 year old man who had been diagnosed as schizophrenic two or three years previously. He was receiving medication in tablet form and by injection to control his hearing of voices and other symptoms. At the same time he was admitted to a residential project for people with mental health problems.

On admission it became apparent that Mike was using cannabis, drinking heavily and gambling excessively. He agreed to help with the last problem but continued both to use drugs and to drink to such an extent that he began to stop taking his medication.

After some weeks, Mike began openly smoking cannabis in the public areas of the house. Although the staff wanted to be sympathetic, they could not break the law by knowingly allowing drug use to continue on the premises. Mike was asked to stop smoking, but he refused. Staff, therefore, began to consider asking him to leave. Unfortunately, the stress of the situation worsened Mike's symptoms and he began lighting fires in the house which put other residents at jeopardy. As a result he was re-admitted to hospital and did not return to the house.

BOB WILLIAMS - a case study

Bob was referred to a Social Services elderly people's team by the staff of his sheltered housing project. He had been placed in this warden-assisted scheme by his local housing department, after presenting to them as homeless. However, as a 69 year old man, he was unusual in that most of his fellow residents were women ten or twenty years his senior. He was also more physically able and active than many of the other residents.

The referral was made because at least once a month Bob would buy a bottle of scotch and become very drunk. In this drunken state he would spend all night banging his cupboard doors loudly and rhythmically. This disturbed and frightened the neighbours. When challenged about these episodes Bob could become violent and abusive and on occasions the police were called to him.

The elderly people's team called in an alcohol and drugs worker to help with the case, but on researching Bob's background it became clear that in the period since the second world war, where he took part in the Normandy landings, he had been intermittently diagnosed as suffering from manic depression, and in recent years he had spent up to eight years in a local psychiatric hospital.

Unfortunately, at some point since his discharge from hospital, Bob's entire mental health records had been mislaid and there was only limited background evidence about his mental health condition. As a result, there then followed a long period during which Bob's disturbed periods were alternately attended to by substance misuse or mental health staff. Neither could agree whether he had a mental health problem or an alcohol problem and as a result there were considerable difficulties in establishing a programme of care.

Bob was, ultimately, asked to leave the residential home and was given a flat in a run down tower block in which he struggled to survive.

ALAN POTTER - a case study

Alan is in his early 40's and has been diagnosed and treated as schizophrenic for the past twenty years. His behaviour gradually eroded his family life to the point that, 15 years ago, he left home and became caught up in a cycle of hospitalisation, homelessness and hostel accommodation.

Over the past five years he has achieved a degree of stability using a range of medication, including depot injections, and support from the local community mental health team. On occasions he has had to return to hospital for short term support. This generally happens in association with his use of alcohol and/or cannabis. His hospital stays have seldom been more than two weeks in length and he had progressed to the point that he had started to establish stable relationships and was beginning to look at a return to work.

Twelve months ago he was again forced to spend some time in hospital after a period of particularly chaotic behaviour. Unfortunately, this forced his housing agency to review his position and they refused to accept him at their facility until he had been fully supported and stabilised. On the other hand, Alan's occupancy of a bed in a hard pressed psychiatric unit also became an issue as it became increasingly difficult to find suitable move-on accommodation.

He had always had an intense interest in cars - he was a trained mechanic - and he helped a number of people with work on their cars while he was in hospital. One afternoon, he "borrowed" a car and was involved in a motoring offence which subsequently went to court. Psychiatric reports were called for by the court, prior to sentencing, and at this point his condition ceased to be described as schizophrenia and was attributed to alcohol.

Alan was sentenced to three months in prison - which he completed without psychiatric support. On his release he had lost the network of community agencies which had previously supported him. He also failed to be picked up by the community mental health team. He was homeless, his behaviour became increasingly chaotic and his situation, all in all, went from bad to worse. He is currently homeless, out of contact with his family and the CMHT, without medication and deteriorating.

TONY WALKER - a case study

Tony is a 45 year-old who has spent all of his adult life either on the road or living in short-term accommodation. He suffered multiple abuse as a child and subsequently found his own sexuality difficult to cope with. Faced with negative situations, his coping mechanism was, and still is, based on either others sexually abusing him, or him abusing others.

Heavy alcohol consumption began in his teens and was well advanced by his mid-twenties. By this time he was homeless in London, and had drifted from one relationship to another - without any form of security. He believed his security lay in the street - where he had no responsibilities - although he craved affection.

At the age of thirty, he began to address his alcohol problem but started to drift from one treatment centre to another - between central London and the North of England. He became increasingly committed to Christianity - which in time began to feed delusion - and his life became increasingly chaotic. He came into a supported housing project at the age of forty and, for the first time in his life, began to address his problems seriously. At first he was dependent on Alcoholics Anonymous for his progress but as he established "roots" the need for psychiatric support became clear. He managed to complete a six-week group therapy programme from which two issues emerged which had to be addressed :

a. His problems were considerably deeper rooted than his alcohol problem and alcohol staff working with him were clear about their inability to give him the full support that they believed he needed.

b. Aspects of his life became increasingly chaotic putting the social gains he had managed to achieve at risk.

His behaviour prompted a series of periods of in-patient treatment with the local mental health services where he was diagnosed as schizophrenic and depressive. He began to make occasional use of community-based resources and periodically relapsed into bout drinking. This in turn made him increasingly depressed and unable to sustain the lifestyle he sought to achieve.

It was difficult both to monitor his progress and support his treatment and recovery within the community - and no long-term psychiatric solutions were presented. There was no liaison between the two disciplines during his periods of treatment in both mental health and alcohol recovery. Both were basically working "blind" of one anothers' therapeutic input. He is currently homeless in South London.

JANE ALEXANDER - case study

Jane was admitted as a psychiatric in-patient for severe paranoid depression on a regular basis from the age of fifteen. On discharge, after her two to three month stays, the medication always increased.

Her alcohol problem began at around the age of sixteen, when she began to frequent gay bars in an effort to establish her sexual identity. The drinking also helped her to overcome the numbness she experienced with the medication and was part of an "after dark" life style which she began when she realised that she had an acute allergic skin reaction to sunlight which was brought about by her high doses of medication.

Her referral to an alcohol treatment unit at the age of seventeen, resulted from concern about Jane's increasingly violent behaviour. It became clear that she was drinking heavily on a regular basis. All her previous symptoms were now accompanied by sudden violent outbursts directed mainly at her surroundings. Her regular self-harm, cigarette burns on her arms and legs, had not changed. Broken furniture and windows at her home clearly concerned her foster parents.

Since the age of ten she had been assaulted and raped four times and later admitted that she had been subjected to abuse by a foster father when she was twelve.

Jane was able to move into a dry house with the support of a local women's group who were addressing her alcohol problems. Her goals were to decrease the medication so she could go to college in daylight and learn to drive, make relationships with lesbian women without frequenting clubs and bars, work on her anger so that she stopped hurting herself and others.

Slow and steady progress resulted in Jane achieving all these goals over a seven-year period. Severe setbacks occurred but each time appropriate resources were dovetailed to address both the mental health and alcohol problems.

In summary, the compounding effects of her prescribed drugs contributed to her alcohol habit. The alcohol precipitated her deep rages and led to increasing hospital admissions as the foster family's tolerance of her mood swings declined. Increasing medication further exacerbated the symptoms. The alcohol treatment unit and the well developed alcohol treatment network in the area broke this circle and also helped the issues around her sexual identity.

ADAM DOLLAND - case study

Adam is the son of a white British mother and an Afro-Caribbean father. Due to his hyperactivity and violent behaviour he has spent most of his childhood in and out of care. From the age of fourteen, he lived in a children's home until he went to a high support project for young people leaving care.

Adam was, by turns, either intelligent, witty and charming or fiercely paranoid and violent. He harboured deep confusion as to whether he was white or black and alternated between two extremes embracing either an all-white culture, lifestyle, and language or a black lifestyle. When in his black culture period he would smoke marijuana. but whatever his state of mind, he drank constantly from the age of fourteen - and almost always spirits. He became known to all the agencies involved with him as a Jekyll and Hyde character.

All these services expressed real fears about the possible outcome of his intense paranoia and violent mood swings. His drinking, in comparison, was taken as a "stage he was going through" and was mostly colluded with, as he was easier to be with and usually very amenable in the early stages of his drinking.

The housing support workers who would be with him night after night saw how alcohol posed risks both to himself and to others. He nearly lost his life, according to their notes, on five occasions. The police endlessly searched him, fruitlessly, for drugs or were for ever detaining him overnight when he was drunk and incapable.

The fire services were accustomed to regular incidents late at night and the casualty department knew him extremely well. He often had extended stays in hospital with broken bones or deep wounds and would emerge from these "dry and happy".

Adam's denial of his drink problem, and an undue focus by all the agencies on his other problems, prevented any real attempt to confront his use of alcohol and the dangers posed to his mental and physical health.

PAM POTTER - case study

Pam's alcohol problem took her into treatment even before her marriage at the age of twenty three. During the six month programme she realised she had suffered from severe depression for many years and accepted the medication that was advised by her doctors.

Subsequently, she married and had two daughters. When she was pregnant with her third child she was beaten up by her husband. The violence continued regularly after the child was born. As a result, she made several attempts to leave with the children, but she finally left home, alone.

Her husband took care of the children until he had a nervous breakdown and they were taken into care. Pam, who had managed to stay dry until now, relapsed and was frequently turned away from the children's home without seeing them.

Social services saw her as a very difficult client, while her husband, on the other hand, was seen as reliable and kind. He visited most days and it was expected that he would ultimately get custody of the youngsters.

Pam returned to treatment and completed a further 12 months in the dry house. Despite her mother's death during this time, and several unsuccessful attempts to regain custody, Pam progressed well and was allowed to visit the children once a week.

After another three months it was agreed that the girls could stay overnight with her on a monthly basis. This proved very positive for both Pam and her daughters, whose schoolwork improved greatly. Her husband, however, became very jealous and very angry. He regularly followed Pam from the children's home and waited outside the dry house in an attempt to speak to her.

Pam remained dry but became increasingly anxious. The children were full of "stories" their father had told them about her. The children's home became concerned and curtailed the overnight stays. Pam despaired of ever being seen as "OK". She increased her medication on the advice of her GP - but was determined not to drink. She maintained her regular visits to see the children.

One day a friend, concerned about Pam's husband's behaviour, met her from the home, in a car. As usual her husband was waiting. He followed them running along the road. He moved in front of the car, threatening them and Pam realised he was very drunk. The car ran him over. According to witnesses it was a complete accident. He was out of control and traffic at the time prevented the driver from taking any other action. The husband was killed outright.

Pam immediately overdosed on a combination of her medication and alcohol and spent nearly six months in hospital. The children were discouraged from visiting. The social worker who had been off sick at the time of the incident was still unwell and temporary replacements came and went. Pam's guilt over the children was too much for her to bear. The children's grief was a double one - particularly for the girls who had become used to regular visits from their mother and enjoyed seeing their father. For a woman who had fought depression, suffered domestic violence, had struggled to resolve an alcohol problem, and was in the process of reclaiming her rights and responsibilities as a mother, there was little understanding or support from those who had to make crucial decisions.

ROGER MAHONEY - a case study

Roger was admitted to a residential facility for people with mental health problems directly from his local acute psychiatric ward. He had been admitted to the ward under a section of the Mental Health Act following a violent incident towards his father and step mother. This in turn had been precipitated by the suicide of his natural mother.

Roger was discharged under the Care Programme Approach and admitted to the residential facility. However, while in the facility it became clear that he was drinking heavily and having difficulty controlling his intake. At times he was hung over and was thus unable to participate in the group programme in the house and thus his placement broke down. He left the home and disappeared from contact with local services.

SECTION 3 - THE NUMBER OF PEOPLE WITH A DUAL DIAGNOSIS

3.1 INTRODUCTION

An essential first task in developing a well-founded, strategic response must be an attempt to develop a picture of the number of clients with a dual diagnosis likely to be encountered in any particular area, whether it be local or national. However, on the basis of the research carried out for this work, it seems that attempts at local data collection are frustrated by three factors:

- an inadequacy of data regarding the prevalence of alcohol and drug problems;
- an absence of local figures for the prevalence of dual diagnosis;
- little information regarding responses to people with a dual diagnosis.

The only significant piece of evidence discovered in the specific geographical area studied was a brief piece of research into the number of people with mental health problems appearing in local police custody suites. In one four week period 206 people appearing in custody suites were interviewed. Of these:

25 were categorised as mentally disordered offenders and

45 were categorised as having substance misuse problems.

Most significantly, of the 25 mentally disordered offenders, over half were categorised as also having alcohol or drug problems. What began as a search for offenders with mental health problems, ended up revealing as much about substance misuse and dual diagnosis.

Other than this valuable data, local investigations undertaken for this study provided little solid information on the prevalence of dual diagnosis. It was, therefore, necessary to acquire national and international data by means of library research, interviews, information technology such as the Compuserve Health Prof. Fora and US database research. Further investigation was undertaken through the Department of Health, the Regional Health Authority for the research area, and the Office of Population Censuses and Surveys. Thus, it has been possible to develop the following estimates of prevalence:

- estimates based on national prevalence data;
- estimates based on data on functional psychosis;
- estimates based on data on substance misuse;

- estimates based on data on homelessness;
- estimates based on data from the criminal justice system.

Beeder and Millman make the most telling comment on the prevalence of dual diagnosis when they write that: "The prevalence ...varies remarkably depending upon the perspectives of the assessment team, the clinical situation in which the evaluation takes place, the severity of the disorders and the patient's perspective."

Different perspectives will inevitably provide very different views on the extent of the problem. The estimates based on these data sources are all open to question, but even assuming a significant margin of error, they present a real challenge to current strategic thinking on the need to address the joint problem of mental health and substance misuse problems.

3.2 NATIONAL PREVALENCE

Government has long been aware of the problematic relationship between drugs and mental health and of the challenges presented by this group to service providers. Yet, until recent times the information on the group has been anecdotal and in particular has been lacking in prevalence data.

However, in 1995, as part of the Survey of Psychiatric Morbidity in Great Britain, the OPCS published their "Report 3 - Economic Activity and Social Functioning of Adults with Psychiatric Disorders". This report addressed a wide range of activities undertaken by adults with mental health problems and, of particular significance for dual diagnosis, a chapter of the report is devoted to the "Use of alcohol, drugs and tobacco." Subsections provided data on the relationship between mental health and alcohol problems (5. 3) and mental health and drug dependence (5.5).

The report identified a number of areas of significance for those working with dual diagnosis, including consumption differences influenced by gender and morbidity. The following findings are of particular interest:

- Women with a neurotic disorder were more likely to be abstainers or moderate drinkers than were women with no disorder (33% against 25%). By contrast, men with a neurotic disorder were more likely to drink heavily (12% against 7%).
- Alcohol consumption was also found to relate to the number of neurotic disorders.
- In general, people with co-morbid mental health disorders were more likely to abstain or drink occasionally than those without mental health problems. However, men with two or more

disorders were more likely to drink over recommended limits (40% against 30%) as well as to drink very heavily (17% compared with 7%).

- A review of ethnicity showed quite clearly that adults in non-white groups were far more likely to abstain or have low levels of consumption.
- The study investigated the prevalence of dependence associated with neurotic disorder. Regular drinkers with a neurotic disorder were more than twice as likely to be dependent as those with no disorder (12% compared with 5%).
- A review of drug disorders showed that adults with neurotic disorders were more than twice as likely to have used drugs in the past compared with those without a disorder (10%:4%). Of particular significance was the finding that drug consumption was especially high among those suffering from phobia, panic and depression.
- Having a neurotic disorder was found to increase the odds of using drugs by a factor of 2.66 but, in this connection, age was the factor of greatest significance. Young adults of 16 - 24 years with neurotic disorder showed an odds ratio of 13.48:1.
- Drug takers with a neurotic disorder were significantly more likely to experience drug dependence (60%) and drug related problems (36%).

Another piece of research - The Epidemiologic Catchment Area study - which involved almost 20,000 semi-structured interviews across the USA (Regier et al, 1990), found lifetime rates for substance misuse among mentally ill people to be 56% for manic depressive illness, 47% for schizophrenia, and 32% for depressive disorder. These rates are 2½ to 5 times those found in the general population. A survey of 171 patients with psychotic illnesses in south London found substance use problems in 36.3% of the group (alcohol problems - 31.6%; drug problems - 15.8%) (Menezes et al, 1996). Young men were at highest risk and substance misusers spent almost twice as many days in hospital as non-substance misusers.

In summary, research confirms many of the conventional beliefs regarding the relationship between drug and alcohol use and psychiatric disorders. In particular, that people with mental health problems are more likely to use drugs and alcohol in a problematic way, and that drug and alcohol misusers are more likely to experience mental health problems.

3.3 ESTIMATION OF PREVALENCE OF DUAL DIAGNOSIS BASED ON FUNCTIONAL PSYCHOSIS

Many of the statistics related to dual diagnosis are decidedly vague. However, the number of people with severe mental illness in the UK is a relatively reliable figure. As a result, it is possible to develop some rough estimates of the prevalence of people with a dual diagnosis based on the probable incidence of drug and alcohol problems among people with severe mental illness, which can be drawn from American data.

The prevalence of functional psychosis in the UK population is 4 per 1000 according to the OPCS. American studies of the severely mentally ill have documented a prevalence of substance misuse among this group as high as 50%. Using this figure it can be estimated that in an area of the UK with a population of 500,000, i.e. the size of an average modern health district, the number of people with functional psychosis and a co-morbid substance misuse problem may be in the order of 665. [This calculation is based on the assumption that a population of 500,000 will contain approximately 334,600 people in the 16-64 population]

This figure may be a substantial underestimate, but it provides a useful starting point from which to review responses. Nowhere in the UK do these 665 dually diagnosable people, whose mental illness must inevitably put them in contact with services, appear to have been identified as a distinct group and, as a result, there is no structured response to them.

3.4 ESTIMATION OF PREVALENCE OF DUAL DIAGNOSIS BASED ON SUBSTANCE MISUSE

The above estimates focus on the combination of psychoses and substance misuse. More accurate estimates of the prevalence of dual diagnosis can be developed by reviewing data on the probable prevalence of substance misuse in a given population.

The OPCS Survey of Psychiatric Morbidity in GB - Bulletin 1 1994 estimates the national prevalence of alcohol dependence to be 4.7% and of drug dependence to be 2.2% in the 16-64 age group. These figures would suggest that within a population of half a million there will be 15,726 alcohol dependent and 7,361 drug dependent individuals.

From US studies (e.g. Co-Morbidity of Mental Disorders with Alcohol & Other Drug Abuse - Epidemiologic Catchment Area Study NIMH/ADA 1990) it is known that for people with an alcohol problem, the incidence of a co-morbid mental health problem is likely to be 37% and for those with a drug problem the incidence will be significantly higher at 53%. Regier et al. 1990 concurs that among the mentally ill there is a frequency of substance misuse above the norm for the remainder of the population but suggest that prevalence will vary dependent upon the presenting illness, for example among schizophrenics the prevalence may be as high as 47%, but for anxiety disorders it is 14.7%, and for affective disorder 32%.

The size of these estimates are supported by British evidence. For example, a study at the Maudsley Hospital suggested that 30-40% of patients with alcohol problems also had an additional diagnosis. (Glass 1988)

Using the American figures it can be estimated that in a population of half a million there will be 5,818 alcohol misusers and 3,901 drug users with a co-morbid mental health problem.

3.5 ESTIMATION OF PREVALENCE OF DUAL DIAGNOSIS BASED ON DATA REGARDING HOMELESSNESS

It is generally recognised that mental health and substance misuse problems have a particularly high incidence among the homeless and inappropriately housed. Numerous research studies in the United States have confirmed a prevalence of some 30% in this client group and some studies in the UK have suggested that the probability of homelessness among dually diagnosed people, although dependent upon diagnosis, may exceed 50%.

The local research for this book produced little hard data to indicate prevalence in these groups. Agency A (a large residential facility for homeless people) suggested anecdotally that the prevalence of mental health problems among their residents approached 60%. Additionally a study of 60 residents, undertaken four years previously, identified 85% as having a drink problem. On the basis of these figures they estimated that between 30% - 45% of the homeless with whom they had contact had a dual diagnosis. As indicated above, research evidence from US research would confirm the validity of this estimate. Even if these local figures are anecdotal, and thus somewhat inaccurate, it does suggest a problem of some significance.

Clearly one of the reasons for both local and national concern about this aspect of dual diagnosis is to be found in the current policy of discharging mentally ill people into the community. Evidence suggests both that more than a third of mentally ill patients discharged from hospital are likely to become homeless, at least temporarily, within six months, and that having a dual diagnosis increases substantially the probability of homelessness following discharge. (Drake & Wallach 1989, Drake Wallach et al 1991.)

3.6 ESTIMATION OF PREVALENCE OF DUAL DIAGNOSIS BASED ON DATA FROM THE PRISON SYSTEM

There are a number of useful indicators of the extent of alcohol and drug problems in prisons nationally. Statistics provided by the Probation Service in the area studied for this book, revealed that out of 259 pre-sentence reports written between 1st July 1992 and 30th June 1993 78 indicated the existence of a serious alcohol or drug problem. This would suggest a figure of 30% of the sentenced prison population with a substance misuse problem. This is without doubt a minimum figure and the actual figure may be very much higher because officers may not always record the information or clients may not reveal the problem.

At the national level Home Office Circular 12/1991 "Throughcare of Drug Misusers" suggests that

12% of sentenced male prisoners

and

24% of sentenced female prisoners

were physically dependent on drugs at the time of their arrest. It goes on to suggest that the rate among remand prisoners is even higher. These figures are obviously lower than those quoted previously because they focus only on prisoners with physical dependence rather than all those with problems related to drugs.

They are not, however, reflected in the notifications by prison medical officers of drug addicts under the Misuse of Drugs Act 1973. Thus in 1991 only 1,747 addicts were notified to the Home Office by Prison Medical Officers, 8% of total notifications. It is important to note that Medical Officers only notify the Home Office when they are actually giving treatment for drug addiction, however these figures do seem to highlight a significant level of under-reporting. (Home Office Statistical Bulletin 19 March 1992)

These latter data emphasise the significant role of illegal drug use, but alcohol is an equally, if not more, significant problem. A survey of male prisoners showed that 45% of those on remand have a significant problem with alcohol, as do 20% of sentenced prisoners (Russell 1978)

All this data highlights the large numbers of people with drug and alcohol problems in the prison system. The importance of this issue has been highlighted by the Government's drug strategy "Tackling Drugs Together" which sets targets for tackling these problems. What is less well-recognised is the extent to which these problems relate to the significant number of people with mental health problems in the prison system.

There is a reasonable body of research into the numbers of people with mental health problems in prisons. Gunn (1991) reports that 2-3% of the prison population have a psychotic illness at any one time. This figure far exceeds the rate of 4 cases per 1000 of the population reported above. On the basis of a study of a sample remand population, one piece of research suggested that more than one in three adult prisoners were "mentally disturbed". (Prins 1994)

While there is no comparable evidence on the extent of dual diagnosis in the prison system, anecdotal evidence from drug workers in the local area studied suggested that at least 60% of drug misusers seen in prison also had a mental health problem. This figure may be an over-estimate, but what all the above data show is the significant numbers of people in the prison system with alcohol or dug problems and the significant number with mental health problems. It is likely, although not proven, that significant numbers of these people overlap. This suggests that the prison system may be a particular area for work on dual diagnosis.

3.7 CONCLUSIONS

There can be no definitive answers about the extent of dual diagnosis in the UK. Partly this is the result of the inadequacy of the data, but, in part, it is also due to the problem of accurately defining dual diagnosis. However, there is enough evidence to suggest that dual diagnosis is a real problem, effecting a significant number of the clients of mental health and substance misuse services.

More importantly, it appears to be particularly prevalent among the homeless population and perhaps among clients of the criminal justice system. Even this limited amount of information suggests a need for action.

3.8 THE NEEDS OF PEOPLE WITH LEARNING DIFFICULTIES - A NOTE

Much of the work on mentally disordered offenders includes people with learning difficulties as an important sub-group and, of course, the Mental Health Act includes those with mental impairment and severe mental impairment as categories of people who are covered by the Act. It could, therefore, be argued that people with learning difficulties should come under the heading of dual diagnosis.

However, this book is not the place to undertake a review of the needs of people with learning difficulties who also have problems with alcohol or drugs. This is a subject worthy of separate and more detailed attention than it has received to date. The case study of Robert Morris highlights that people with learning difficulties can and do have substance misuse problems. The authors simply wish to highlight that this is a need which has been very poorly addressed by the substance misuse field to date.

ROBERT MORRIS - case study

Robert is a 34 year old man with learning difficulties. He has lived his life between his parents' home and a variety of institutions.

His father was a heavy drinker who frequently beat his mother. Robert often drank heavily when at home, but drank little in the large specialist hospital he lived in until recently.

Last year he moved into a small community home. He shares this house with several other residents and there is a staff team to support them.

Shortly after moving in, Robert began to drink heavily on a regular but not continual basis. These drinking bouts would be accompanied by verbal abuse to people in and out of the house and sometimes threats of violence.

The staff tried reasoning, cajoling and persuasion to encourage Robert to change his drinking. However, all these efforts failed. Finally the staff decided to put Robert under threat of dismissal. If he drank again he would have to return to the hospital. This had the desired effect. Robert stopped drinking.

Unfortunately the staff now face a dilemma. Robert appears to be under control in the house, but what will happen when he moves into his own accommodation? Because he is being forced not to drink, he isn't learning anything about dealing with alcohol. What will happen if that control is removed?

SECTION 4 - A REVIEW OF THE EXISTING LITERATURE ON THE NATURE OF DUAL DIAGNOSIS

4.1 INTRODUCTION

"Dual diagnosis", like its partner "co-morbidity", is becoming a buzz phrase, liable to misunderstanding. The term "diagnosis" is defined as the "determination of the nature of a diseased condition; identification of a disease by investigation of its symptoms and history; the formal statement of this" (Shorter Oxford English Dictionary). Additionally, in clinical practice, a diagnosis is useful to describe conditions and communicate about them; to indicate what treatments might be appropriately ·offered; and to offer an idea about prognosis in the light of past experiences of the conditions.

The term "dual diagnosis" (El-Guebaly, 1990), however, does not imply a simple cause and effect relationship between substance use and mental illness, rather it has four subtypes (adapted from Lehman et al, 1989):

1. A primary mental illness with subsequent (including consequent) substance use (eg depressive disorder self-treating with alcohol).

2. A primary substance misuse with psychiatric consequences (eg amphetamine-induced psychosis).

3. A dual primary diagnosis (eg LSD misuse and manic depressive illness).

4. A common aetiological factor causing mental illness and substance misuse (eg post-traumatic stress disorder leading to both alcohol misuse and depressive disorder).

The term "co-morbidity" is also used in this context and is a more general title to describe the co-occurrence of symptoms or disorders. The phrase "Mentally Ill Chemical Abuser" (MICA) is also used in North America. This book will use the term "dual diagnosis" unless an alternative is clearly more appropriate.

Psychiatric diagnosis is hierarchical, moving from organic brain disorder (eg a brain tumour, Korsakoff's syndrome, delirium tremens), to severe mental illness (eg schizophrenia, manic depression), to non-psychotic illness (eg anxiety neurosis, most forms of depressive disorder), and finally to personality problems (eg maladaptive personality traits and personality disorder). This means that, for instance, it is not good practice to diagnose schizophrenia (severe mental illness) if there is a brain tumour (organic brain disorder) unless there is clear evidence of the mental illness significantly preceding the tumour, because tumours can produce psychotic symptoms. Similarly, people with schizophrenia commonly complain of depression, but this is due usually to inadequate treatment of the schizophrenic illness rather than a separate depressive disorder. Finally, persistent substance misuse with its attendant behavioural and social problems may mimic personality disorder, although problems remit on abstinence (unlike personality disorder which, by definition, is enduring). Substance use and associated disorders fits uneasily into this hierarchy, as it can be a symptom of, a cause of, or just associated with, mental disorder. This chapter will take a logical progression through the hierarchy of psychiatric diagnosis in relation to substance use, concentrating on severe mental illness as this is implicitly the focus of many dual diagnosis issues.

4.2 ORGANIC BRAIN DISORDERS

The main types of organic brain disorder associated with substance use are:
- abstinence syndromes;
- toxic states, including psychotic reactions;
- and brain damage.

These are considered below.

4.2.1 Abstinence syndromes

Delirium tremens (DT's) is the best known abstinence syndrome, although it is still misdiagnosed in clinical settings. It starts between twenty-four and seventy-two hours after the last alcoholic drink and follows the more generalised feelings of anxiety, insomnia, loss of appetite and paranoia that can occur in withdrawal. There are visual hallucinations, tremor, clouding of consciousness, paranoid delusions and epileptiform convulsions. Over fifty years ago delirium tremens were common and there was a 25% mortality rate, now it is relatively rare because of better general health and better care. Misdiagnosis of DT's as a paranoid psychosis is dangerous because many types of antipsychotic medication (eg chlorpromazine (Largactil), thioridazine (Melleril)) increase the likelihood of epileptiform convulsions and because sedative medication (eg benzodiazepines) and vitamin supplements (eg thiamine - vitamin B1) may not be given.

Benzodiazepine withdrawal, as well as withdrawals from barbiturates and other sedatives such as chlormethiazole (Heminevrin), produces similar effects to DT's with severe panic attacks and depressive symptoms in the early stages of abstinence. Convulsions are common in abrupt abstinence. There may be perceptual distortions which can include hallucinations and there may also be delusional beliefs.

Abstinence after high levels of stimulant use (eg amphetamines, cocaine) can cause unpleasant mood changes (especially depression), drug craving and severe tiredness. Prolonged depressive symptoms may indicate an underlying depressive illness requiring specific treatment. Suicidal thoughts are common and there is an increased risk of suicide. The psychological and physical features of opioid withdrawal are not associated with an organic brain syndrome, nor is cannabis withdrawal.

4.2.2 Toxic States Including Psychotic Reactions

Substances are used and misused for their psychoactive effects. Almost any substance can cause adverse effects, for example, even water overload can result in biochemical and mental changes. Moreover, there are individual variations to the responses to different substances. Thus, substance use associated with psychotic features can not imply simple cause and effect.

Hallucinogenic substances such as LSD (lysergic acid diethylamide) and "magic mushrooms" generate brief psychotic episodes lasting a few hours. However, the psychotic episodes may last several weeks, requiring hospital admission and antipsychotic medication. Maguire and Fahy (1991) have reported a similar psychosis associated with Ecstasy (MDMA).

Amphetamines have a similar effect on the brain to the naturally occurring neurotransmitters noradrenaline and dopamine. There are a large and wide variety of substances with amphetamine-like actions. They produce an acute, overexcited state of anxiety and restlessness together with hallucinations and delusions (Connell, 1966). Prolonged usage at high doses may result in a longer-lasting psychosis that resembles schizophrenia and may require hospital treatment. A similar psychosis occurs with heavy cocaine misuse, including so-called "formication" (hallucinating the feeling of insects on the patient's skin) sometimes being perceived.

The relationship between cannabis use and psychosis has aroused much debate. Cannabis is the most widely used illicit drug in many countries. Evidence cited by Mathers and Ghodse (1998) and Newman and Miller (1992) indicates that moderate use by those with stable backgrounds is not very harmful, but that usage for more than a year at higher doses increases the risk of chronic intoxication or acute psychotic reactions, especially in those who are socially disadvantaged, culturally dislocated, or psychiatrically ill.   The evidence for a "cannabis psychosis" is contradictory, and there is even less support for the so-called "amotivational syndrome" in which tranquil lethargy accompanies regular, heavy usage.

Auditory hallucinations and delusions akin to those found in schizophrenia occur in alcoholic hallucinosis. This is neither schizophrenia nor delirium tremens, but Cutting (1978) found that, on following up patients with this condition, 27% remained well, 19% acquired a diagnosis of schizophrenia, and 21% developed a depressive or manic illness.

Morbid jealousy is a poorly understood paranoid syndrome (Michael et al, 1995) associated with regular, heavy drinking. It includes distressing and unacceptable irrational thoughts, emotions and behaviours around a partner's sexual infidelity and may end in homicide. It is also associated with depressive features, and is influenced by personality factors.

4..2.3 Brain Damage

Brain damage occurs mostly in relation to alcohol use, rather than drug use. Exceptions include neurological toxicity of volatile substances, such as solvents, (Sudbury and Ghodse, 1990) and psychosis and dementia associated with AIDS (secondary to injecting drug use).   There is conflicting evidence about brain damage associated with prolonged, heavy benzodiazepine use, although cognitive deficits have been noted by Golombok et al (1988).

There are three forms of brain damage associated with alcohol misuse: Wernicke's encephalopathy; Korsakoff's psychosis; and alcoholic dementia.   The first two are often taken together since they are, in that order, the acute and chronic syndromes caused by haemorrhages in the hypothalamus and other central parts of the brain involved in registering new memories. They occur when, having used alcohol as its energy source, the brain cannot use glucose to provide energy because of thiamine deficiency (vitamin B1) due to alcohol misuse and a poor diet. Wernicke's encephalopathy consists of a reduced level of consciousness (delirium), unsteadiness (ataxia) and paralysis of muscles controlling eye movements (ophthalmoplegia). The longer term consequence is Korsakoff's psychosis, memory loss for both before and after the brain damage occurs. There is difficulty recalling memories in the correct order, leading to confabulation, when true memories are incorrectly sequenced and linked by falsifications.

Alcoholic dementia is the result of a more global brain damage affecting problem-solving and complex activities eg learning to ride a bicycle for the first time (due to frontal lobe damage); visual/spatial activities are affected eg building a scale model (non-dominant parietal lobe); and there is a more general deterioration involving memory loss. The mechanism for alcoholic dementia is a direct toxic effect of alcohol on the brain, rather than thiamine deficiency in the Wernicke-Korsakoff syndrome (Lishman, 1990).

4.3 SEVERE MENTAL ILLNESS
This category includes
- schizophrenia,
- manic depressive illness and other severe depressive disorders.

These two categories will be considered in turn.

4.3.1 Schizophrenia
It has been shown that substance misuse leads to overdiagnosis (misdiagnosis) of schizophrenia (Cohen, 1995), resulting in inappropriate treatment being given with correspondingly poor outcomes. Such diagnoses should always be delayed until abstinence is confirmed and psychotic symptoms are then seen to persist. Regular urine testing may be required to screen for continuing substance use, even in relatively secure in-patient facilities (illicit drugs enter prisons despite even greater safeguards). More generally, substance misuse in people with schizophrenia is associated with increased rates of violence (Bartels et al, 1991), suicide (Drake and Wallach, 1989), non-compliance with treatment (Pristach and Smith, 1990) and overall poor prognosis (Drake and Wallach, 1989). Overall, the clinical outcome of patients who misuse substances is worse than those who do not.

There are a number of reasons for increased risk of substance misuse amongst severely mentally ill people. The move from institutional to community care has increased exposure to drugs and alcohol and there is a downward social drift associated with both schizophrenia and substance misuse (Smith and Hucker, 1994). There is widespread, increasing availability and acceptability of drug use in society and these people may be the least able to resist peer pressure to use drugs. Selzer and Lieberman (1993) have suggested that the knowledge that psychotic symptoms can be reproduced by a drug may engender a paradoxical sense of control to people with severe mental illness.

There is a common perception that substance use may be a form of "self-medication" of psychotic symptoms: Castaneda et al (1991) found that, apart from cocaine, which worsened psychotic symptoms, other drugs, including alcohol, had no net beneficial or detrimental effects on conditions, although individuals reported wide variations in effect.

Treatment of schizophrenic patients who misuse substances is complicated by the failure to recognise substance misuse by relevant caring agencies (El-Guebaly, 1990) and the failure to acknowledge it by clients themselves (Smith and Hucker, 1994).   In the USA, people are often better treated by psychiatric services as substance misuse services are too confrontative (Ridgely et al, 1990).   However, many substance misuse services in the UK are closely aligned with psychiatric teams, facilitating, at least in theory, closely integrated, shared care.   Often the first stage in treatment is detoxification, usually as an inpatient, allowing clarification of the diagnosis and subsequent optimisation of pharmacotherapy. Engagement and recognition of substance misuse can be difficult and might involve motivational interviewing techniques (Miller and Rollnick, 1991). Drake et al (1993) concluded that the following components are important in the effective treatment of people with severe mental illness and substance misuse:

- assertive outreach;
- close monitoring;
- supportive accommodation;
- careful timing of treatment interventions;
- taking a long-term therapeutic perspective;
- and optimism.

In the USA, Galanter et al (1994) have developed a range of dual diagnosis facilities including a dual diagnosis ward, a halfway house and an ambulatory day programme.   In the 27-bed dual diagnosis ward there is conventional psychiatric assessment and pharmacological treatment. Additional aspects are based on a peer leadership approach coupled with professional treatment, and provide multiple levels of care based on the needs of respective patients.   There are educational groups focusing on relapse prevention techniques and HIV/AIDS education.   Twelve step groups (Alcoholics Anonymous and Narcotics Anonymous) are held daily. Aftercare issues are discussed in discharge planning groups.   Patients are encouraged to comply with the programme by a system of rewards for participation in the various therapeutic elements (a token economy method of behaviour modification); this is implemented through peer leaders.

The halfway house is a 30-bed residential unit aimed at homeless men with a dual diagnosis.   The format is adapted from that of a drug/alcohol-free therapeutic community, supplemented by multidisciplinary input.   Groups are less confrontational than those in a non-dual diagnosis facility, recognising that these patients are usually psychologically fragile. The ambulatory day programme has about 40 places and is the least intensive of the three components. It is also based on a drug/alcohol-free therapeutic community. Clinical experience of this programme over six years is encouraging but the need for proper staff education and support is emphasised.

4.3.2 Manic Depression and Severe Depressive Disorder

Whilst the prognosis for combined substance misuse and depressive disorder is worse than for either condition alone, appropriate treatment depends on appropriate assessment. Typically, abstinence from alcohol and drugs 'for at least four weeks is highly desirable to allow remission of depression secondary to substance use and the unmasking of the primary depressive disorder (Brown et al, 1995). However, some people continue to use drugs and alcohol, often these who do not receive adequate treatment. A patient with a severe depressive disorder may require compulsory assessment and treatment, but others can be offered motivational interviewing to help them change their attitudes to continuing substance use. Repeated failure to respond to such interventions raises the possibility of hidden maintaining factors including personality disorder.

Suicide and deliberate self-harm are significantly increased in substance misusers (Hasin et al, 1988). Often they do not seek or receive treatment for suicidal behaviour. There is some evidence that carers in substance misuse institutions have difficulty addressing or discussing suicidal risk (Wolk-Wasserman, 1987). Recent interpersonal loss or conflict (within six weeks) is more common in alcohol misusers who complete suicide (41%) than in completers with a primary depressive disorder (20%) (Rich et al, 1988).

4.4 NON-PSYCHOTIC MENTAL ILLNESS

Alcohol and sedative drugs generally enhance mood at low doses because of anxiety reduction and create a disturbed mood (dysphoria) at higher doses. Most depressive symptoms are organic, neurochemical effects or transient psychological responses akin to brief stress reactions (Davidson and Ritson, 1993). They may be particularly marked during sustained intoxication or when alcohol/drug levels are falling (Schuckit and Monteiro, 1988). Tolerance leads to increasing the dose to achieve the same effect. Substance misusers may complain of depression as psychological, relationship, financial and physical problems supervene. These depressive symptoms usually remit on abstinence, especially for alcohol misuse (Brown and Schuckit, 1988). Persistence of depressive symptomatology after 2-3 weeks' abstinence suggests the presence of a depressive disorder. The self-medication hypothesis suggests that depressed people self-treat with alcohol and other substances, this being a preferable, more socially acceptable alternative to psychiatric care. However, there is little evidence to support this in depressed inpatients (Castenada et al. 1994).

Anxiety disorders, both free-floating and phobic, may incorporate an element of alcohol misuse and depression (Mullaney and Trippett, 1979). Regier et al (1990) found that 23.7% of people with an anxiety disorder had significant substance misuse during their lifetime. Post-traumatic stress disorder commonly presents with substance misuse (Evans and Sullivan, 1995). In both cases abstinence from substance use is prerequisite for accurate identification and treatment of the mental disorder.

Most drug treatment for mental illness is negated by coincidental substance misuse. However, specific serotonin reuptake inhibitors (eg fluoxetine (Prozac), paroxetine (Seroxat) are preferred where there are biological features of depressive disorder (eg early morning waking; mood worse in the morning than the evening; loss of the capacity to enjoy life (anhedonia)) because of relative safety in overdose and relatively lower sedative effects compared to tricyclic antidepressants (eg dothiepin (Prothiaden), amitriptyline (Tryptizol)). Tricyclic antidepressants are also more likely to lower the threshold for epileptic fits during alcohol, benzodiazepine and barbiturate withdrawal. Lithium prophylaxis (eg lithium carbonate (Priadel)) has no established place except where there is evidence of a recurrent mood disorder with biological features of a depressive disorder or manic phases (Murphy, 1992).

Abstinence from alcohol may be assisted by an alcohol-sensitising agent such as disulfuram (Antabuse) (Chick et al, 1992) or, possibly, by craving reduction using naltrexone (Volpicelli et al, 1995). Naltrexone has a more conventional use in the prevention of relapse into opiate misuse by blocking opiate receptors in the brain so that no pleasurable reactions occur.

Cognitive-behavioural treatments are applicable to anxiety, depression and substance misuse (Beck et al, 1993). Specific programmes address current symptoms and may offer structured relapse prevention techniques. Marital and family therapy may be of benefit if the mental disorder is not severe (Evans and Sullivan, 1990). Alcoholics Anonymous and Narcotics Anonymous also offer a well-established, structured approach to alcohol/drug misuse and can support abstinence while a depressive/anxiety disorder receives treatment. Desensitisation techniques such as cue exposure can fulfil a similar function (Drummond et al, 1995). However, when considering which treatments are most indicated, it is very important to consider the likelihood of compliance in relation to motivation and psychological impairment due either to mental illness or to brain damage (eg alcohol-induced).

4.7 PERSONALITY PROBLEMS

Personality disorder is strongly associated with substance misuse. Regier et al (1990) found that 83.6% of people with an antisocial personality disorder in the ECA study had had significant substance misuse during their lifetime. Multi-impulsive personality disorder (seen as a form of bulimia nervosa) (Lacey and Evans, 1986) and borderline personality disorder are linked by definition to substance misuse because impulsivity (including fatal and non-fatal deliberate self-harm), nihilistic feelings and substance misuse itself are integral facets of these disorders (Beck et al, 1993). There is now a clear case for the routine screening for personality disorders in substance misusers (Ghodse, 1995), given increasing evidence about the effectiveness of short-term psychotherapies (Winston et al, 1994) and these should be available to patients in substance misuse treatment programmes.

Substance misuse is strongly associated with criminal behaviour. Gudjonsson and Petursson (1990) have noted that the marked increase in homicide in Nordic countries mirrors the increase in per capita alcohol consumption. A study of violent offences committed by people with schizophrenia (Lindqvist and Allebeck, 1989) shows that over half were certain or probable substance misusers and that 40% of the offences were committed whilst intoxicated.

4.8 CONCLUSIONS

"Dual diagnosis" is a useful term that crystalises ideas about the combination of substance misuse and severe mental illness in particular, although it is liable to be misunderstood. It can raise awareness of the potential for misdiagnosis and, therefore, help to target sub-optimal treatment. For example, organic brain disorders may occur in substance misusers and may be missed by unwary professionals.

Substance misuse is commonly associated with severe mental illness and there are a number of psychosocial reasons for this. Treatment for people with substance misuse and severe mental illness is specialised and must be adapted to their special needs (including psychological fragility and poor motivation) and vulnerabilities. Depression is a symptom commonly reported by substance misusers and sometimes may be part of a depressive disorder rather a transient phase during substance use, detoxification and recovery. Dually diagnosed people are at high risk of suicide and this must be assessed and addressed, even though it may be very difficult, ultimately, to prevent.   Anxiety symptoms are common and are susceptible to behavioural and cognitive-behavioural interventions.   There is a strong link between substance misuse and criminal behaviour, especially violent acts. Personality disorders and substance misuse are closely associated and very difficult to treat.   However, since some personality disorders rely on substance misuse as a diagnostic criterion, they have limited validity in this group.

More research is undoubtedly required to supplement the work outlined above, which is mainly from North America.   Social conditions and service configurations are markedly different in Britain and this undermines the generalisability of these research findings, although still giving much guidance as to what needs to be done.

SECTION 5 - A REVIEW OF RELEVANT NATIONAL GUIDANCE

5.1 INTRODUCTION - UNRECOGNISED OPPORTUNITIES

This section outlines the main areas of legislation and national guidance which might impinge on the issue of dual diagnosis. Almost all of these focus primarily on the mentally ill. Some specifically mention issues related to substance misuse, but more frequently they offer opportunities which those concerned about substance misuse and mental health problems might want to exploit. For example, the Health of the Nation's concern for reducing the level of suicide is an excellent opportunity to press the link between dual diagnosis and suicide. Supervision Registers offer opportunities to provide more co-ordinated programmes of care for this client group - an opportunity which may be being spurned at present.

5.2 THE MENTAL HEALTH ACT

The Mental Health Act 1983 is the key piece of legislation on the care of people with mental health problems. Its central role is to allow for the compulsory detention of a person in hospital for assessment or treatment if it is:

- in the interests of his or her own health;
- in the interests of his / her own safety;
- for the protection of other people.

Only one of these criteria needs to be satisfied. The Act places these decisions in the hands of appropriately qualified doctors and social workers.

The Act is very specific about what constitutes a mental health problem. It is one of:

- mental disorder,
- severe mental impairment,
- mental impairment or
- psychopathic disorder.

The Act goes on to say that:

"Nothing ...above shall be construed as implying that a person may be dealt with under this Act as suffering from mental disorder, ... by reason only of promiscuity or other immoral conduct, sexual deviancy or dependency on alcohol or drugs."

(Mental Health Act 1983 p.2)

43

While this statement is a clear indication that there is no intention to allow people to be detained under the Act purely because of their use of alcohol or drugs, it does leave vague the question of how to handle the often blurred interaction and inter-relation between a mental health problem and substance misuse. If alcohol consumption acutely worsens the state of someone with a mental health problem, does that allow them to be brought under the Act?

These are questions which will need to be answered if dual diagnosis is to be adequately addressed. However, they will demand answers not simply at the political level but also at an ethical level. The alcohol and drug field has always had doubts about the effectiveness of compulsory treatment. Will it be acceptable to begin to consider bringing at least one group of substance misusers under the powers of the Mental Health Act?

5.3 BUILDING BRIDGES

In 1995 the Department of Health issued a guide entitled "Building Bridges - A Guide to Arrangements for the Care and Protection of the Severely Mentally Ill". Its purpose was to encourage collaboration between agencies in order that severely mentally ill people receive the best possible care. It provides a useful summary of the main pieces of legislation and guidance covering the severely mentally ill and examines the role of voluntary and statutory agencies in caring for such people.

As such it should provide useful material for those concerned about a severely mentally ill person who also has a substance misuse problem. More pleasingly it also recognises the existence of dual diagnosis. The guide says: "Drug and / or alcohol misuse can have a significant impact on the well-being and risk status of severely mentally ill people. People with a dual-diagnosis of mental illness and drug or alcohol misuse may require treatment from both sets of specialist services, and close links need to be maintained at provider level to ensure that such care is properly co-ordinated." (Building Bridges - Dept. of Health 1995 p.42)

The reference is small but it is a significant step towards solid action on this client group. It also seems to support the need for closer co-operation and liaison between mental health and substance misuse services which is one of the themes of this book.

5.4 SUPERVISION REGISTERS

Supervision Registers were established under Department of Health Circular HSG(94)5. It requires all specialist psychiatric health service

44

providers to identify and provide information on clients who are potentially at risk of harming themselves or others. The intention is to ensure that people at risk can be identified both to themselves and ensure that local services focus resources on those who have the greatest priority.

The local research for this book highlighted a failure to place people with a dual diagnosis on the register. This may well be a matter both for concern and urgent attention. Although the register is clearly aimed at the severely mentally ill, "Building Bridges" indicates that those with a dual problem can be registered. In one of its question and answer sections the book offers this guidance:

"Do patients with alcoholic dependence fit into the category of 'severe and enduring mental illness', and are they therefore liable to be put on a register?

We would not regard patients who suffered from alcohol dependence alone as coming within the above definition. If, however, a patient develops a mental disorders such as Korsakoff's Syndrome, as a result of alcohol dependency, then he or she may indeed fall within the category of 'severe and enduring mental illness'". (Building Bridges - Dept. of Health 1995 p.72)

While this information mentions neither drug problems nor any other form of mental health problem other than the alcohol-related Korsakoff's Syndrome, the guidance does seem to suggest that severely mentally ill people with a dual diagnosis could and should be placed on the register.

5.5 CARE PROGRAMME APPROACH

The Care Programme Approach was introduced in 1991 to ensure that those who have experienced severe mental health problems appropriate and, above all, co-ordinated care and support in the community. Its details are laid out in Circular HC(90)23. Its main requirement is that all patients referred to specialist psychiatric services have a care programme which is appropriate to their needs, and agreed by care staff and family as and when possible.

Additionally, and in support of the above circular, Discharge Circulars HC(89)5 and HSG(94)27 lay down the requirement that the discharge of patients who are likely to be a danger to themselves or to others is carefully handled. Although none of these circulars specifically address the issue, when applied to dually diagnosed patients, they should enable them to be monitored and supported both through treatment and rehabilitation.

5.6 HEALTH OF THE NATION

The Health of the Nation, which was published in 1992, is the Government's strategy for health in England. It sets mental health as one of five key areas and establishes three main targets:

- To improve significantly the health and social functioning of mentally ill people.
- To reduce the overall suicide rate by at least 15% by the year 2000.
- To reduce the suicide rate of severely mentally ill people by at least 33% by the year 2000.

Given the high suicide rate among people with a dual diagnosis, which is alluded to elsewhere in this book, it would seem that the Health of the Nation targets would be a useful vehicle for arguing for greater attention to be paid to this issue.

The document pays little attention to the links between mental health and substance misuse. While recognising the significant role of benzodiazepine tranquillisers in both treating and exacerbating depression and anxiety, it does not mention the part played by the misuse of illegal drugs. The Health of the Nation report does recognise that reducing alcohol consumption would help achieve the targets. It acknowledges that 10% of psychiatric patients have alcohol problems and recognises the significant role played by alcohol in suicide, but it does not mention the existence of dual diagnosis per se.

5.7 MENTALLY DISORDERED OFFENDERS - THE REED REPORT

The key document in the planning of responses to Mentally Disordered Offenders in recent years is the Reed Report which was published in 1992. The full title of the report is: "A Review of Health and Social Services for Mentally Disordered Offenders and Others Requiring Similar Services". The committee was chaired by Dr. John Reed.

The final report is deceptive since it runs to only about a hundred pages. However, those pages contain 276 separate recommendations, and the report is simply the summary of the findings of nine working parties each of which produced a sizeable report of its own. These background documents are much more informative than the inevitably cursory summary, and interested parties should make efforts to read these papers.

The report makes a specific recommendation about substance misuse: "Active links should be made between services for mentally disordered offenders and those for substance misusers, including strategic co-ordination between multi-agency groups for mentally disordered offenders, area committees for the criminal justice system and regional co-ordinating systems for alcohol and drug misuse services." (recommendation 101)   While this advice is only one item among a huge number of recommendations it is a useful vehicle for developing work on dual diagnosis.

A more subtle link is the kind of services that Reed recommends should be developed to meet the needs of mentally disordered offenders.   In the public mind, mentally disordered offenders will bring associations with the inmates of special hospitals like Rampton and Broadmoor.   Reed deals with this client group, but pays more attention to the offender committing minor crimes.   The emphasis of the report is that "wherever possible mentally disordered offenders should receive care and treatment from health or social services rather than the criminal justice system." (recommendation 1)   In other words: diversion.

To achieve this much-needed diversion, Reed commends schemes which identify clients in police stations, courts and prisons and then moves them into alternative services.   All of these tasks are objectives that the alcohol and drug field has been trying to further with its own client group for some considerable time.   Reed offers a tremendous opportunity to develop such important services jointly with mentally disordered offender services.

The great disappointment of the Reed report was that no new funds were made available at the time of its publication.   Nonetheless, the report offers a vehicle to develop services for alcohol and drug users in a new and exciting way.

5.8 THE TASK FORCE TO REVIEW SERVICES FOR DRUG MISUSERS

Commonly known as the "Effectiveness Review" this document was published in May 1996 as part of the Government's Drug Strategy.   It was a thorough review of the effectiveness of treatment for drug misusers in this country.   The report is an interesting document in itself, but it also highlights the role of dual diagnosis.   In one of its recommendations it writes:

"Purchasers and providers should ensure that people working in both drugs and mental illness services are aware of the need to identify and respond to problems of combined psychiatric illness and drug misuse." (8.72)

This recent publication should be used as a spur to developing work on dual diagnosis.

5.9 INQUIRIES INTO VIOLENT DEATHS

Over the last few years concern over deaths in which people with a history of mental illness have killed others, has led to a number of published inquiries. The best known of these is the "The Report of the Inquiry into the Care and Treatment of Christopher Clunis" which was published in 1994. This report specifically excludes drug or alcohol use as a contributory factor in Christopher Clunis's behaviour, however other reports do provide examples of behaviour which might be linked to a dual diagnosis. The most recent of these is the inquiry into the murder of Jonathan Newby.

"On 9 October 1993 Jonathan Newby, a twenty-two year old graduate, working as a volunteer for the Oxford Cyrenians at Jacqui Porter House in Rectory Road, Oxford, was stabbed in the heart by John Rous, a resident in the house. Jonathan Newby died as a result of this injury" (p.3)

This death prompted the establishment of an independent inquiry into the circumstances surrounding the death. This report listed a number of factors which, by 9 October 1993 were acting on John Rous. These included:

"i. John Rous had been under pressure to repay a £20 loan to MIND. He did pay but was not pleased to do so;

ii. Resident B's behaviour was affecting John Rous. He was upset and disturbed when in Jacqui Porter House; his sleep was disturbed as B would run up and down stairs;

iii. John Rous's medication was wearing thin, he had been due to receive his depot injection on 8 October, and this was postponed to 11 October at his request.

iv. John Rous's appointment with Dr. Agulnik on 5 October had been postponed, and John Rous was unhappy about this;

v. He had increased his intake of alcohol and possibly cannabis;

vi. By 8 October 1993 John Rous was in a state of high expressed emotion. The skills of those providing immediate support, namely the workers at Jacqui Porter House and Angela Stannard, were inadequate to deal with such a state. They displayed no awareness of the increase in the level of John Rous's agitation, restlessness and anger;

vii. The inadequacy of the procedures and arrangements at Jacqui Porter House meant that the elements supporting John Rous in those days prior to Jonathan Newby's death were paper thin, there was a total failure to provide a supportive environment for John Rous." (p.140)

The report concludes by asking agencies involved in residential care of the mentally ill to consider:

"19.3.1 The programme of in-service training for employed staff and for volunteers should be intensified and be better directed to the needs of the severely mentally ill and the staff caring for them. To be more specific, without implying their relative importance or the amount of time that should be spent on each the following should be considered:

i. the signs and symptoms of major mental illness

ii. understanding and learning to talk with severely mentally ill people,

iii. substance abuse and its management: alcohol and drugs

et al." (Report of the Inquiry into the Circumstances Leading to the Death of Jonathan Newby - July 1995 p.151-2)

This brief but tragic extract highlights both the complexity of dual diagnosis, but more significantly for this section that there are references to alcohol and drug-related issues hidden across a wide range of official reports.

SECTION 6 - RESPONSES TO PEOPLE WITH A DUAL DIAGNOSIS IN ONE AREA OF THE UK - A STUDY

6.1 INTRODUCTION

This study into the nature of, and responses to, dual diagnosis in one part of the UK took place in late 1994 and early 1995. It was conducted largely on the basis of interviews with key professionals, as well as a review of local strategies, agency policies and other relevant documentation.

The area studied was a large local authority covering both rural and suburban populations. Although it had a level of affluence above the national average, it still had pockets of deprivation and a small but significant homeless population.

6.2 STRATEGY AND POLICY

The beginning of a coherent response to any problem must be the development of a strategy. There is no national strategy on dual diagnosis at either a political or a professional level. While this might be disappointing, it is not surprising. The more immediate concern is the absence of either strategy or policy responses to dually diagnosed clients at the local level in the research area.

All provider units interviewed acknowledged the existence of clients with a dual diagnosis. However, none were able to articulate in precise terms either a strategy or a policy for addressing this issue. The common response was expressed in terms of the competence of the unit to deal with problems to a particular level of seriousness. The level varied but in none of the organisations reviewed, was it related to a specific and precise assessment of the nature and extent of dual diagnosis.

One member of an addiction service felt that "staff cannot cope with co-morbidity", having neither the time nor the skills necessary. The outcome for services seemed to be that alcohol/drug units adopted a policy of dealing with "minor" mental health problems, particularly neuroses, in-house or by the involvement of a GP. The range of "minor" problems included in this encompassed depression, anxiety and phobias. All would be addressed as an adjunct to addiction treatment.

Other approaches included linking with sections of the mental health services, either in hospitals or the community, to obtain a response for a patient through a GP, community mental health team (CMHT) or specialist nurse or doctor from a psychiatric unit. What does not appear to have happened is the production of a specific and comprehensive treatment plan based on a full assessment of psychiatric and substance misuse status. Only one unit appeared to be moving towards a more comprehensive approach. The attitude to dually diagnosed people appeared to be that they were a problem, rather than a separate, specific and legitimate client group.

Where major disabling mental health problems co-existed with an addiction problem, intervention strategies appeared to be based on the assumption that until the mental health problem had been addressed there was little or nothing that could be done by a substance misuse service to help the patient. The problem of dealing with psychoses or other major and disabling mental health problems was seen as being beyond the training and resource competence of a substance misuse service even where that service was staffed by qualified mental health nurses and medical personnel.

The view appeared marginally different within the acute psychiatric services. It was acknowledged that a significant proportion of patients had problems of dual diagnosis. However, treatment appeared to centre upon addressing either mental health issues or upon detoxification. The consequence for one service, a mental illness day hospital, was described by one respondent in terms of the hospital being "clogged up with drug and alcohol people". Another respondent was certain that the CMHT's picked up on the "end of the line" clients, whom nobody else wanted or could handle.

There was no suggestion that people who were referred did not receive treatment. The issue was that those who referred with dual diagnosis problems were assessed by services either as drug users with minor mental health problems, or as people with major mental health problems who happened to have a substance misuse problem. Their dual diagnosis was not seen as a specific problem and therefore deserving of a planned and comprehensive response.

One service recognised the need to address this issue and was seeking funding for a specialist worker to develop a more effective response in this area. Whilst this is obviously a welcome change and will support a close focus on dual diagnosis issues it is important to recognise that the need may not be for another parallel service for dual diagnosis, but rather for a better response from, and integrated use of, the current services.

6.3 ASSESSMENT

The full assessment of dual diagnosis appeared to be a rare phenomenon in the area studied. However, the need for change had been recognised by the regional substance misuse team who were undertaking research on this topic, and within the area, the potential impact of mental health problems on the treatability of substance misuse problems had been recognised in the social services department's assessment procedures for admission to specialist treatment services.

A review of the quality of assessment for people with a dual diagnosis in the research area found the following situation:

1) Where an alcohol or drug problem was identified it appeared that physical health was reviewed and appropriate treatment offered for both the physical problem and the dependency.

2) Dual diagnosis of mental health and substance misuse problems appeared to be assessed less accurately for reasons which included:

- the absence of formal tools for assessing dual diagnosis;
- deficiencies in training throughout the health and welfare system on this issue;
- a lack of confidence among primary care staff in dealing with either substance misuse or mental health problems;
- a lack of confidence among specialist substance misuse staff in dealing with mental health problems;
- a failure to identify people with a dual diagnosis;
- an absence of a formal strategy for the dual diagnosis of mental health and substance misuse;
- a lack of central direction to address the issue.

As has been said, the process for assessment of clients was not standard across the area studied. The evaluation of mental state might take place in a variety of settings and with tools ranging from inpatient assessment by psychiatric services through to assessment by workers in local drug services. The assessment of substance use might be carried out by CMHT's, social workers or substance misuse specialists in community or hospital settings.

There was no direction from the local purchasing consortium on the process to be applied. However, the assessment process for community care funding of a person with a drug or alcohol problem provided an adequate assessment of the history of substance misuse and a brief glance at psychiatric and psychological profile. Yet there was no contracted requirement for the assessors to have been trained to identify and respond to dual diagnosis.

Thus the present patterns of assessment in the area studied were clearly not adequate to the task of determining an appropriate package of intervention for the dually diagnosed patient. A review of some of the tools used shows quite clearly that the emphasis within specialist drug services is on drug issues.

In Agency B (a specialist in-patient substance misuse treatment unit), an initial assessment consisting of six pages of questions sought to profile drug use and physical health, one page with four broad questions and a medication list outline the psychiatric profile. The unit did not have a comprehensive strategy for identifying or working with dually diagnosed patients. However, it was anticipated that the looked-for approval of funding for a specialist worker will greatly improve the response at all levels to dual diagnosis.

Agency C, a community substance misuse team, operated on the basis that the vast majority of drug users are distinguished from their peers by their drug use, and that mental health is of no greater prevalence in the drug using community than in the general population. Where a problem was identified the team hoped to pick it up and deal with it without labelling. The treatment decision in this agency was made on the balance of morbidity, but "much would be contained within the team". Agency C applied the General Health Assessment as a matter of course.

Agency D, a large in-patient alcohol unit, was developing an improved assessment service, to be supported by a four bed detoxification facility. Whilst it was the view of the consultant in charge that mental state is best assessed on a general psychiatric ward, there was considerable movement in the view of what could be treated within the unit. The workers in the unit acknowledged that working with depressed patients was a problem for them (currently estimated at 15-20% of the patient group) and florid schizophrenia was not considered suitable for treatment within the agency. It was intended to take most patients from the detoxification facility provided that any mental health problems could be treated. This was clearly an encouraging move. It suggested that dual diagnosis was acknowledged, would be assessed while detoxification was under way, and that a treatment programme would be developed on site.

Agency E, a community drug team, had recently developed a new set of criteria for assessment. The topics to be covered offered a reasonably comprehensive overview of a client's personal and substance use history. However, it did not appear likely to provide a mental health profile to match this. As with the other substance misuse services, whilst frequently delivered by staff with mental health skills and qualifications, there was potentially a measure of tunnel vision in the approach to dual diagnosis.

Within mental health services, the quality of assessment of dual diagnosis was also questionable. Hospital services appeared to respond either to detoxification needs or to mental health needs on the basis of whichever was the primary or secondary problem. As indicated below this was not helpful when dealing with comorbid problems and both issues should have been addressed pending the conclusions of observation.

There was considerable opportunity for sound assessment in CMHT's. The profile of these teams, which could include specialist substance misuse workers, provided the skills for assessing dual diagnosis and their community location was useful for assessing behaviour and social competence. However, in spite of this opportunity, these teams did not appear to be identifying and working with the large numbers of dually diagnosed clients known to be in the community. The complexity of dual diagnosis appeared to result in onward referral. However, the quality of the assessment process remained doubtful further along the treatment process.

One CMHT reviewed whether the client was known to the substance misuse services. If so, the case was viewed as a substance team referral. Another respondent expressed the view that the effective role of the CMHT was that "if there was motivation to work on the problem it would go to substance misuse, if not, to the CMHT".

6.4 TREATMENT

There were, perhaps inevitably, very few examples of treatments for people with dual diagnosis separate from the usual range of services offered by substance misuse and mental health services.

Agency A (the residential facility for homeless people) accepted that a high percentage of its residents had multiple problems. They, therefore, operated two detoxification beds and twelve rehabilitation beds and, both as a matter of necessity and as a matter of organisational policy, worked with dual diagnosis clients.

Agency D (the in-patient alcohol treatment unit) was moving towards the delivery of a more comprehensive throughcare service commencing with detoxification and assessment of mental state during detoxification. This would allow staff to determine whether to continue treatment of dual diagnosis patients or whether the level of mental health morbidity is beyond the competence of the unit.

Agency B, an in-patient drug and alcohol unit, was trying to appoint a specialist worker to improve the quality of its dual diagnosis service.

However, these were all units with an expertise in dealing with drug and alcohol issues. They were only able to process comparatively small numbers of patients in total, and the majority of those people were not dually diagnosed.

6.5 PRIMARY AND SPECIALIST WORKER TRAINING

For many years there have been serious deficiencies in the training of health and social care staff in the identification and treatment of alcohol and drug problems. Concern about AIDS / HIV and the accelerating incidence of drug dependence have resulted in these issues beginning to be addressed at many levels in the community. The Home Office, Department of Health and training establishments have all moved to ensure the provision of better drug and alcohol training. The latest initiative, the Government White Paper on "Tackling Drugs Together" is precipitating further improvement in the nature and extent of training and encouraging greater local cohesion in developing strategies for responding to substance misuse. However, mental health has remained something of a poor relation in reviewing training needs, and training in dealing with the dual diagnosis of mental health and substance misuse appeared non-existent in the research area.

If people who have a dual diagnosis of substance misuse and mental health problems are to be identified, properly assessed and offered interventions appropriate to their needs, it will be essential that primary workers in all relevant settings are provided with relevant training to ensure that the process of care is initiated as soon as possible rather than waiting for it to touch specialist services.

Several respondents in the research area identified a lack of training in the dual issues of mental health and substance misuse as a barrier to effective responses within specialist agencies. Although specialist staff were clearly aware of such dual diagnoses they were an extremely small group, already overstretched in dealing with the flow of more straightforward clients and, arguably, were unlikely to be able to offer a more extensive assessment and intervention service.

6.6 THE LACK OF A DUAL DIAGNOSIS FOCUS

There was little focus on dual diagnosis. Within the specialist services the problem was acknowledged and addressed where identified. However, current responses appeared to be based on identifying the "major" problem and reacting to it, rather than identifying, analysing and responding to dual or multiply diagnosable problems.

6.7 DUAL DIAGNOSIS AND THE CRIMINAL JUSTICE SYSTEM

Agencies involved in criminal justice, particularly the police and probation services, were aware of dual diagnosis as a feature of their work. Services for this group fall into the category of work with mentally disordered offenders (MDO's). In this broader area much more work has been undertaken.

In common with many other probation, health and social service areas, agencies in the research area had recently undertaken extensive work on mentally disordered offenders. A strategy, a handbook on how to handle MDO's and an investigation into multi-agency working in the area had all been recently written and were typical of much work produced up and down the country in the last two or three years. Together these documents offered many useful suggestions for working with this client group. However, whilst the local strategy acknowledged the relationship between substance misuse, mental health and criminality, it does not specifically address the needs of the dually diagnosed offender.

The recent work on MDO's at both local and national level has offered many useful suggestions for ways in which the criminal justice system might respond more appropriately to the needs of this client group. These are equally applicable to those whose offence is related to a dual diagnosis. The suggestions include:

- the need for mental health issues to be identified by police, probation, the courts and the prison system;
- the importance of pursuing a sentence which acknowledges the profile and needs of this group;
- the importance of trying to divert from custodial sentencing;
- careful assessment before discharge into the community.

All of these approaches were being examined in the research area, but none was specifically being targeted at dually diagnosed clients.

6.8 SUMMARY OF FINDINGS

Services for substance misusers and for people with mental health problems in the area studied did not operate in such a way as to provide a seamless and fully customised service for people whose needs straddle this professional divide. Clients who were dually or multiply diagnosable were offered the service which was deemed appropriate to address the most pressing or problematic symptoms. However, work undertaken with this client group elsewhere has begun to point to the need for addressing the dual problems in a unified and structured manner.

Those with a dual diagnosis of substance misuse and mental health problems did not receive a service which was tailored to their needs:

- their dual diagnosis was unlikely to be recognised ;
- they were unlikely to be fully assessed;
- it was improbable that they would receive treatment based on their dual diagnosis.

Where dual diagnosis was acknowledged, the services available were unlikely to offer a therapeutic programme which dealt with this in an integrated way. People suffering from psychoses almost always had their psychosis dealt with in a psychiatric setting, while their dependency was dealt with by another therapeutic service.

Where people misusing substances required treatment for lesser mental health problems, such as depression, this was likely to be dealt with by their GP. However, it was improbable that a consultant psychiatrist would assess the mental health problem and recommend an integrated treatment regime.

Although florid psychosis would always produce a response from the psychiatric or drug services it was clear from the investigation that minor mental health problems would, if identified, be dealt with in passing. Whilst this may be appropriate at one level, it is a strategy which could result in a failure to identify and respond to minor depressive illness, particularly in juveniles. Juvenile suicide, clearly an indicator of a mental health issue, is frequently associated with substance use or misuse. However, no services appeared to have a preventative strategy which responded to low grade depressive illness when associated with substance misuse. The national figures for juvenile suicide would suggest that this issue should be addressed as a matter of some urgency.

The criminal justice services were clearly able to identify dual diagnosis among the larger group of mentally disordered offenders. This was encouraging and should provide a valuable base on which to develop services targeted at this group.

SECTION 7 - RECOMMENDATIONS DRAWN FROM THE LOCAL STUDY

7.1 INTRODUCTION - THE CURRENT SITUATION

The information obtained during the writing of this book does not highlight a satisfactory or balanced response to people with a dual diagnosis at either a local or a national level. The number of individuals who suffer from co-existing substance misuse and mental health problems is high and given the high incidence and poor prognosis for those receiving treatment represents a significant drain on treatment resources.

The social, criminal and treatment problems generated by people with a coexisting substance misuse problem and mental health problem were acknowledged in all agencies approached during this assignment. Police, probation, social services, mental health, housing and specialist alcohol and drug services in both the statutory and non-statutory sectors were able to identify a range of service challenges raised by this client group. However:

- the vast majority of clients experiencing the problems of coexisting substance and mental health problems appeared either not to be identified by any services or received treatment which was tailored to address mainly one element in their comorbid status;
- clients received a variable response across the research area dependent upon the agency they approached, and upon the ability of that agency to identify, assess and treat or refer the problems which were identified;
- the identification process was not standardised and there were no clear criteria for defining a dual diagnosis;
- it is clear that staff, whilst aware of the issue as a feature of their work, have not been required to develop skills, knowledge or understanding of dual diagnosis and possible responses to it;
- purchasers offered no clear specification or expectation of a particular service response to dual diagnosis by provider unit;
- the competence of the data systems available to those working in the research area appeared in large part untested by service managers, and were clearly not used to design services for people with a dual diagnosis.

7.2 A MODEL FOR A RESPONSE

The ideal system may be developed from that typically proposed for addressing drug client needs. In such a model clients are recognised to move through a well-defined process including:

- identification by one of the front line services, or as a result of self-referral;
- assessment of the presenting problem, and identification of other relevant mental, physical, social and economic issues;
- treatment, in terms of detoxification, therapy, medication as appropriate;
- rehabilitation in a residential or non-residential setting with appropriate support.

The ideal system of care should be based on clients receiving the best possible service at all stages in the process from acquiring a problem to having it resolved.

7.3 IDENTIFICATION

Dual diagnosis is largely concealed by a failure of identification. In part it appears probable that this is due to training deficiencies and a lack of confidence on the part of care staff that they have the skills to address the "other half" of the presenting problem. The consequence of this is often a rapid referral to the agency which specialises in what is perceived to be the main problem.

It is also apparent that the assessment systems being used within drug and mental health services will not in all cases identify the true nature or extent of a dual diagnosis. It is known from previous research that GP's do not always recognise the drug or alcohol component in a presenting physical or mental health problem.

Identification of dual diagnosis in the area studied for the research took place at some levels. However, the quality of that identification was variable and dependent upon location, lifestyle and the nature of presenting problems.

The key issues, therefore, in achieving the identification of clients with multiple disorders are :

- The ability and willingness of workers to identify dually diagnosable clients;
- The frequency and quality of the client's contact with services;
- The residential status of a client;

- The domestic circumstances of the client;
- The client's history of offending and imprisonment.

Each of these is explored below.

7.3.1 The Ability and Willingness of Workers to Identify Dually Diagnosable Clients

The identification of problems requires that staff have both knowledge and confidence. However, in this context the present patterns of training in health and welfare services do not support the identification of dual diagnosis. This should be addressed by those responsible for in-house training and for communicating skills and knowledge requirements to training establishments.

Those planning, purchasing and providing training for mental health and substance misuse service providers need to consider whether:

- front line staff have the skills necessary to identify -
  alcohol problems?
  drug problems?
  mental health problems?
  combinations of these problems?
- front line staff are aware of procedures to be taken following identification of the above?
- front line staff are confident that they will receive support from line management in seeking further assessment of identified clients?
- organisations have the resource capacity to meet the reasonable response requirements of staff who identify dependency, mental health or dual diagnosis?

7.3.2 Frequency and Quality of Contact with Services

Some individuals with quite severe mental health problems as well as drug and alcohol problems may have little or no contact with services. This is not to say that they do not present symptoms, rather that their depression or anxiety, for example, may be ascribed to drinking or drug use by the few contacts they do have with services.

The precursors for "professional" contact, with police, probation, social services, or primary health care, might include problems such as criminal activity, sickness, bizarre behaviour or suicide attempts. Obviously, making first contact under these circumstances must be seen as a failure on the part of services to identify and address potential difficulties before problems arise.

One proactive solution to this is to improve the quality and breadth of outreach work. An analysis of the costs of failing to identify and prevent a potential suicide against the costs of investment in staff would justify a reasonable expenditure in this area. The effectiveness of outreach work in the drug field has been amply proven, for example, a single detached drugs worker in a Midlands town identified over 120 amphetamine users who were unknown to services (unpublished data).

It may also prove beneficial to broaden the scope of such initiatives to incorporate a wide range of work with young people. One area in which identification commonly fails is that of juvenile suicide. It is clear that juveniles who attempt suicide, successfully or unsuccessfully are experiencing mental health problems and frequently such suicides involve drink or drug misuse.

7.3.3 Residential Status

All surveys of dual diagnosis identify a particularly high incidence among the homeless due to the inability of people with problematic mental health and behavioural problems to support a stable lifestyle.

Given the high profile of the homeless, and the fact that they are readily located in hostels, hospitals and the community it should be easy to target dual diagnosis in this group. However, many clients have chosen to move away from mental health and other statutory services and their problems therefore remain unaddressed other than in settings such as the facility for homeless people (Agency A) examined in the research area.

7.3.4 Domestic Circumstances

Substance misuse and mental health problems clearly impact significantly on behaviour. It is, therefore, probable that dual diagnosis can be readily identified whilst people are in stable relationships. However, it is also recognised that these factors contribute to family break-up. One means of identifying potential problems and offering intervention may be to encourage improvement in the education and training of relationship counsellors and relevant staff within the domestic courts.

7.3.5 History of Offending and Imprisonment

As has already been said, a significant proportion of people coming into the criminal justice system are problem drinkers or drug misusers. Of these, many will experience problems ranging from emotional disorders to psychoses, with their disorder being a major contributory factor in their offending.

The opportunity for detecting and intervening in problems at this stage has been recognised by the prison and probation services, the health service and police among others. Of particular relevance is the application of the requirements of the Mental Health Act 1983 to work within the criminal justice system. As one report points out: "After discharge (from hospital) they are likely to need regular and possibly urgent multi-disciplinary reassessments by the community team. This should involve at least the consultant, CPN, social worker or care manager and always the key worker." (Strategy for MDO's in Surrey - Standing C'tee on MDOs - Nov '94)

In particular, where a dual diagnosis is indicated, prison pre-release plans should be developed which acknowledge both the likelihood of relapse and of suicide.

7.4 RECOMMENDATIONS

7.4.1 Service purchasers should review their contract targets to ensure that dual diagnosis is addressed. Specifications should incorporate performance indicators or outcome measures.

7.4.2 Police custody sergeants should be asked to monitor the number of clients presenting dual diagnosis problems since this seems to offer a valid and highly valuable source of data on a large proportion of this group.

7.4.3 Primary worker training should incorporate training in the recognition and handling of dually diagnosed clients.

7.4.4 The Probation Service should ensure that the training provided to officers in dealing with MDO's also addresses the issue of mental health, substance misuse and offending problems.

7.4.5 Service providers should conduct a training needs analyses for staff in therapeutic contact with clients. This analysis should assess the ability and confidence to work with dually diagnosed people.

7.4.6 Based on the above analysis training on dual diagnosis should be offered to all relevant staff.

7.4.7 Any training planned by Drug Action Teams in the context of "Tackling Drugs Together" should include this topic.

7.4.8   Substance misuse and mental health service providers should review their approach to the dual diagnosis of mental health and substance problems.   Particular attention should be paid to accurate assessment of the mental health component of all presenting problems by substance misuse services.

7.4.9.   There should be a programme of work to ensure that GP's are aware of dual diagnosis and the range of available responses.

7.5 ASSESSMENT

The assessment of clients with a dual diagnosis is particularly challenging and few workers would have the skills to achieve a full assessment of all aspects of a dual or multiple diagnosis.

There are a number of issues which need to be considered for the assessment of people who misuse psychoactive substances and who have a comorbid mental health problem.   They may:

- have complex needs including domestic or accommodation crises;
- move between areas frequently;
- self-refer to agencies not in their area;
- avoid contact with statutory services;
- need to be provided with services many times;
- behave unpredictably and not fit easily into the assessment and care management systems designed to meet the needs of other client groups.

There are strong arguments that assessment should be conducted by people with experience in substance misuse and mental health.

The dual diagnosis group cannot therefore be viewed by mental health services as merely a problem, but rather should be approached as a major demand on the resources of all mental health services both in hospitals and in the community.   Given a probable prevalence of such magnitude, staff in mental health services should always question whether substance misuse is one of the problems contributing to the morbidity of all those who are referred.

In reviewing the patterns of responses to dual diagnosis in the research area it was clear that there was a lack of structure and clarity in the assessment process. This need not be the case since there is a growing literature around the assessment of dual diagnosis.   The literature contains some fundamental guidelines which can be broadly broken down into phases of intervention, the first two of which are assessment oriented:

Phase one - Preliminary contact:
      Assessment of physical, mental and dependency state
      Acquisition of basic data including
            medical & psychiatric history
            personal data
            confirmation of referral data
      Agreement on confidentiality as appropriate
      Agreement on preliminary intervention/referral

      Phase Two - In-patient assessment, if appropriate:
      Observation
      Assessment of general health
      Management of acute detoxification
      Management of acute psychiatric problems
      Medical intervention for general health as appropriate

The core assessment task in this phase is to assess the possibility of dual diagnosis on the basis of patient reaction to withdrawal and psychiatric stabilisation. The literature stresses the importance of not allocating primacy to either disorder, but providing concurrent treatment for both.

Phases Three and Four are the treatment and rehabilitation phases which are addressed below.

7.6 RECOMMENDATIONS

7.6.1. Mental health services should review their procedures for the assessment of substance misuse.

7.6.2. Consideration should be given by mental health and substance misuse services to the development of specific protocols for the processing of dually diagnosed people.

7.6.3. The assessment tools used by services should be reviewed and amended where appropriate to ensure that the balance of the assessment reflects the problems of the presenting client or patient, rather than the skills and interests of the assessing agency.

7.6.4. Social Services Departments should ensure that Community Care assessment processes and forms reflect the concern for a balanced picture of the mental health and substance misuse of referred clients.

7.6.5. Purchasers and service providers should agree, develop and install improved data systems to enable the provision and use of data on dual diagnosis.

7.6.6.   Given the absence of data and the awareness of field workers of the high prevalence of undetected and untreated dual diagnosis in the homeless and inappropriately housed population, health and social services should consider the appointment or designation of staff to operate an outreach service. The objectives of this service should be:

- to establish contact with those dually diagnosable people who are not in receipt of treatment
- to identify the extent of this group
- to advise on the development of future strategy for this group.

7.7 TREATMENT

"It is the treatment issue, probably more than any other, where the rhetoric of hope substantially exceeds the knowledge which has accumulated" (Penick et al. 1990)

The research for this book has highlighted at least four problems with current treatment for people with a dual diagnosis:

- Treatment method within the UK currently emphasises work with one side or the other of a dually diagnosed problem.   It is acknowledged that this is changing.   However, experience elsewhere indicates that both elements of a problem may best be treated in a parallel manner pending further assessment.
- Treatment of this group with psychoactive drugs is notoriously difficult due to poor compliance with treatment regimes.
- The treatment services offered to dual diagnosis people do not appear to be designed and applied in response to their comorbid status. Rather, they are dealt with according to the concerns of the service with whom they are in contact and the availability of resources.
- Treatment services such as hospital based mental health services are frequently failing to identify and respond to the great number of people experiencing dual daignoses in other settings.

The preliminary review of services and limited data in the research area confirms the above pattern. Addressing dual diagnosis as a problem deserving of a specific set of responses was not common within either the mental health or dependency services. The reasons for this may not be particularly complex, but rather the result of therapeutic distance between the two services, and a consequent and radical difference in the approach to treatment.

Substance misuse services have not seen themselves able to apply their largely behavioural therapies to mental health clients. Where people exhibit bizarre, challenging or depressed behaviours they have been referred for psychiatric intervention. On the other hand, mental health services have all too frequently viewed the mental health problems of presenting problem drinkers and drug users as a symptom of excessive consumption or as an obstacle to effective psychiatric intervention. The "dry them out and chuck them out" approach was, for many years, a standard and only slightly unfair description of detoxification in psychiatric hospitals.

The outcome has been an effective denial of dual diagnosis in favour of a consequential approach to substance misuse and mental health, with the assumption being made that either one could not treat the psychiatric problem before the patient was detoxified, or that the psychiatric problem had to be resolved/stabilised before there could be any hope of working with the substance misuse.

Recent research has proved conclusively that regardless of which is the "primary" problem, the degree of severity of the secondary problem is a sound predictor of treatment outcome. It is therefore illogical to attempt to address either problem in isolation. Accurate and early identification of comorbid substance and mental health problems is essential.

7.8 AN IN-PATIENT TREATMENT MODEL

What is also clear, as was highlighted in the literature above, is that American services are beginning to achieve positive treatment outcomes with this client group. The methodology, which in part reflects approaches elsewhere, is based upon a multi-stage treatment model designed specifically for the dually diagnosed. It is laid out here in a much clearer way to allow ready consideration by service purchasers, planners and providers. The treatment programme is based around three distinct clinical units:

1.   an inpatient dual diagnosis ward offering:
   psychiatric management
   psychoeducational groups
   support groups
   discharge planning groups
   introduction to stages 2/3

2.   a 30 bed halfway house providing
   a strict abstinence regime
   1:1 and group therapeutic support
   up to 6 months residence

3. an ambulatory day programme including
   social rehabilitation
   psychiatric care
   womens & perinatal health groups

The project has been held up as an example of good practice in the United States. The significance of this model lies in its development as a strategic response by mental health services to an issue which is being addressed in a piecemeal fashion in the UK. It is also significant in that the service has been developed to address the needs of a group of patients whose psychiatric profile and drug use parallels that of the dually diagnosed patient group in the UK. In short, it represents a challenge to local and national thinking and strategy for responding to co-morbidity.

By way of comparison the situation in the research area and, in particular, the experience of residents of Agency A (the facility for homeless people) in their contact with hospital services is that there is "massive conflict between the need for mental health and detoxification beds. Mental health is winning hands down"

This is not helpful for dually diagnosed people who need to have their mental health and detoxification issues addressed in parallel. There is a need for services to review the possibilities for amending their approach to the delivery of inpatient services to the dually diagnosed.

7.9 SERVICE RANGE

A key finding from research is that there is a broad range of types of dual diagnosis, reflecting the range of mental illnesses and the range of abused substances. It is therefore important to ensure that there is a range of responses available to address the complexity and variety of dual, or indeed multiple diagnoses. However, for services to be developed to this degree of consumer sensitivity it will be essential for staff to be trained, and identification and assessment systems developed, to an appropriate standard.

7.10 RECOMMENDATIONS

7.10.1. Providers should seek to ensure that their staff have access to a full range of information regarding the treatment of dual diagnosis with particular focus on current research into dual diagnosis subtypes.

7.10.2. Treatment services should review research findings into outcome, with particular focus on the importance of matching therapies to patients in terms of prescribing practice, use of psychotherapeutic approaches, preferred drugs of abuse and mental health profile.

7.10.3. A member of staff should be designated to ensure that services are updated on changing knowledge and practice in the treatment of dual diagnosis.

7.10.4. Inpatient services should review their approach to the handling of dually diagnosed patients.

7.11 REHABILITATION / SUPPORT

Given the paucity of data on dual diagnosis in the research area, and the comparative scarcity of information on outcome from other sources, it is not possible or reasonable to address rehabilitation in other than general terms. Dually diagnosed people present a range of complex treatment problems. The ability of this group to conform to maintenance medication regimes is low, and psychotherapeutic approaches to mental health issues may conflict with best practice in addressing substance misuse. It is generally found that as a group dual diagnosis clients are more dysfunctional and respond less well to therapeutic approaches over time.

However, it is possible to identify a range of support systems which appear to work in both mental health and substance misuse fields. It is safe to assume that at the very least these services will be required to provide the best chance of survival for dually diagnosed patients on their return to the community.

Not surprisingly, given the current identification rates, psychosocial profile and relapse rates of this client group there appear to be few, if any, dually diagnosed people who move through the healthcare system to demand rehabilitation and support in the community.

One area where some services are provided is that of the criminal justice system and, .n particular, services for mentally disordered offenders. There was a firm intention among the key agencies in the research area that this group would receive throughcare and aftercare of a standard appropriate to their needs. For this to be delivered it will be important, as indicated earlier, for all relevant staff to receive training. It is also essential that those responsible for care planning and assessment of dually diagnosed people within the criminal justice system have both the competence and resources to identify and deliver suitable services.

In the absence of research into the needs of the dually diagnosed it is difficult to provide verifiable data regarding the rehabilitative needs of this group. However, much is known about mental health needs, and about drug and alcohol rehabilitation. It is, therefore, possible to suggest topics for further investigation by teams who will work with dual diagnosis in the future.

These needs are:

- Accommodation - this will necessarily include a full range of services from re-entry services through specialist supported accommodation to independent living either self -supporting or with landladies/landlords;
- Support - both in the form of rapid access to advice and counselling, plus ongoing therapy, group and day centre support where appropriate;
- Training/retraining in social skills, domestic management and work skills;
- Health care - to ensure continuation and control of medication where required;
- A safety net - which can pick people up when a mental health or substance misuse relapse occurs.

Clearly, these needs will require more investigation over time once the dually diagnosed patient group has been identified and is being worked with more effectively.

7.12 RECOMMENDATIONS

7.12.1 Using the outreach worker recommended above the needs of dually diagnosed people should be identified. These needs should be classified in terms of: accommodation; therapeutic support; social support; survival skills; employment / work rehabilitation; income; recreation/leisure; safety net.

7.13 FINAL WORD

Whether it is agreed that dual diagnosis is a valid category or not, there are clearly significant numbers of people in the UK who have both some kind of mental health problem and some kind of substance misuse problem. It is also clear that these people are not receiving the best treatment and care.

This book has identified one set of problems in one are of the UK. These may not be the only problems and the only solutions. However, there can be no doubt that action is necessary at both the national and the local level in order to reduce the costs of dual diagnosis to individuals, families, health and social services, and society as a whole.

SECTION 8 - USEFUL ADDRESSES AND BIBLIOGRAPHY

8.1 USEFUL ADDRESSES

Alcohol Concern
Waterbridge House
32 Loman Street
London SE1 0EE

Alcoholics Anonymous
PO Box 1
Stonebow House
Stonebow
York
YO1 2NJ

AL-ANON
61, Great Dover Street
London SE1 4YF

Standing Conference on Drug
Abuse
Waterbridge House
32 Loman Street
London SE1 0EE

Institute for the Study of Drug
Dependence
Waterbridge House
32 Loman Street
London SE1 0EE

MIND (National Association for
Mental Health)
Granta House
15-19 Broadway
London E15 4BQ

National Schizophrenia
Fellowship
28 Castle Street
Kingston
Surrey KT7 1SS

Good Practice in Mental Health
380-384 Harrow Road
London W9 2HU

SANE
199-204 Old Marylebone Road
London NW1 5QP

Northern Ireland Association for
Mental Health
80 University Street
Belfast BT7 1HE

Wales MIND
23 St. Mary Street
Cardiff CF1 2AA

Scottish Association for Mental
Health
Atlantic House
38 Gardner's Crescent
Edinburgh
EH3 8DQ

Manic Depression Fellowship
8-10 High Street
Kingston
Surrey KT1 1EY

8.2 - BIBLIOGRAPHY

This section consists of both the books and articles referred to in the text, plus a number of other works which may be of interest to those wishing to research further into this area.

Allan C. - Psychological Symptoms, Psychiatric Disorders and Alcohol Dependence Amongst Men and Women Attending a Community-based Voluntary Agency and an Alcohol Treatment Unit - British Journal of Addiction, vol. 86, no.4, pp419-427

Allan C. - Alcohol Problems and Anxiety Disorders: A critical review - Alcohol and Alcoholism, vol. 30, no.2, pp145-151

Bartels SJ, Drake RE, Wallach MA, Freeman DH. Characteristic hostility in schizophrenic outpatients. Schizophrenia Bulletin 1991;163-171.

Beck AT, Wright FD, Newman CF, Liese BS. Cognitive therapy of substance abuse. New York: Guilford Press, 1993.

Brown MA, Inabra RK, Gillin JC, Schuckit MA, Stewart MA, Irwin MR. Alcoholism and affective disorder: clinical course of depressive symptoms. American Journal of Psychiatry 1995;152:45-52.

Brown SA, Schuckit MA. Changes in depression among abstinent alcoholics. Journal of Studies on Alcohol 1988;49:412-417.

Cantwell R, Harrison G. Substance misuse in the severely mentally ill. Advances in Psychiatric Treatment 1996;2:117-124.

Castaneda R, Galanter M, Lipshutz H, Franco H. Effect of drugs on psychiatric symptoms among hospitalised schizophrenics. American Journal of Drug and Alcohol Abuse 1991;17:313-320.

Casteneda R, Lifshutz H, Galanter M, Franco H. Empirical assessment of the self-medication hypothesis among dually-diagnosed inpatients. Comprehensive Psychiatry 1994;35:180-184.

Chick J, Gough W, Falkowski W, Kershaw P, Hore B, Mehta B, Ritson B, Ropner R, Torley D. Disulfuram treatment of alcoholism. British Journal of Psychiatry 1992;161:84-89.

Cohen IS. Overdiagnosis of schizophrenia: role of alcohol and drug misuse. Lancet 1995;346:1541-1542.

Cohen P. - The Right Diagnosis - Community Care - 30th June 1994

Connell PH. Clinical manifestations and treatment of amphetamine type of dependence. Journal of the American Medical Association 1966;196:718-723.

Cooke et al. - Something to Lose - Case Management for MDOs. - Jnl of Mental Health - 1994 3,59-67

Cutting J. A re-appraisal of alcoholic psychoses. Psychological Medicine 1978;8:285-295.

Davidson K, Ritson EB. The relationship between alcohol dependence and depression. Alcohol and Alcoholism 1993;28:147-155.

Drake RE et al. - Homelessness & Dual Diagnosis - American Psychologist - Nov '91 pp1149-58

Drake RE, Wallach MA. Substance abuse among the chronically mentally ill. Hospital and Community Psychiatry 1989;40:1041-1045.

Drake RE, Bartels SJ, Teague GB, Noordsy DL, Clark RE. Treatment of substance abuse in severely mentally ill patients. Journal of Nervous and Mental Disease 1993;181:606-611.

Drew T. & King M. - The Mental Health Handbook - Piatkus -1995

Drummond DC, Tiffany ST, Glassier S, Remington B. Cue exposure in understanding and treating addictive behaviours. In: Drummond DC, Tiffany ST, Glassier S, Remington B, eds. Addictive behaviour: cue exposure theory and practice. Chichester: John Wily and Sons, 1995.

Duffy J. and Kreiman N. - Risk Factors for Suicide and Undetermined Death among Inpatient Alcoholics in Scotland - Addiction, vol.88, no.6, pp.757-766

El-Guebaly N. Substance abuse and mental disorders: the dual diagnosis concept. Canadian Journal of Psychiatry 1990;35:261-267.

Evans K, Sullivan JM. Dual diagnosis: counselling the mentally ill substance abuser. New York: Guilford Press, 1990.

Evans K, Sullivan JM. Treating addicted survivors of trauma. New York: Guilford Press, 1995.

Farrell M. and Lewis G. - Discrimination on the Grounds of Diagnosis - British Journal of Addiction, vol.85, no.7, pp883-890.

Galanter M, Egelko S, Edwards H, Vergaray M. A treatment system for combined psychiatric and addictive illness. Addiction 1994;89:1227-1235.

Ghodse AH. Substance misuse and personality disorders. Current Opinion in Psychiatry 1995;8:177-179.

Glass I. and Jackson P. - Maudsley Hospital Survey: Prevalence of Alcohol Problems and Other Psychiatric Disorders in a Hospital Population - British Journal of Adiction, vol.83, no.9, pp1105-1111.

Golombok S, Moodley P, Lader M. Cognitive impairment in long-term benzodiazepine users. Psychological Medicine 1988;18:365-374.

Gudjonsson GH, Petursson H. Homicide in the Nordic countries. Acta Psychiatrica Scandinavica 1990;82:49-54.

Gunn, Maden & Swinton - The Number of Psychiatric Cases Among Sentenced Prisoners - Home Office - 1991

Hasin D, Grant B, Endicott J. Treated and untreated suicide attempts in substance abuse patients. Journal of Nervous and Mental Disease 1988;176:289-294.

Johnson B.A. - Substance Misuse Among Psychiatric Hospital In-patients - Irish J. Psychol. Med. 1990 7 (2) p114-117

Lacey JH, Evans CDH. The impulsivist: a multi-impulsive personality disorder. British Journal of Addiction 1986;81:641-650.

Lehman AF, Myers CP, Corty EC. Assessment and classification of patients with psychiatric and substance abuse syndromes. Hospital & Community Psychiatry 1989;40:1019-1030.

Lehman et al - Prevalence & Patterns of Dual Diagnosis Among Psychiatric Inpatients - Comprehensive Psychiatry - Vol35 No2 March '94 pp 106-112
Lindqvist P, Allebeck P. Schizophrenia and assaultative behaviour: the role of alcohol and drug abuse. Acta Psychiatrica Scandinavica 1989;82:191-195.

Lishman WA. Alcohol and the brain. British Journal of Psychiatry 1990;156:635-644.

Madden JS. Psychiatric syndromes associated with alcohol and substance misuse. In: Chick J, Cantle R, eds. Seminars in alcohol and drug misuse. London: Gaskell Press, 1994.

Maguire P, Fahy T. Chronic paranoid psychosis after misuse of MDMA ("ecstasy"). British Medical Journal 1991;302:697.

Mathers DC, Ghodse AH. Cannabis and psychiatric disorder. Current Opinion in Psychiatry 1988;1:350-352.

MDO Handbook - Mentally Disordered Offenders Project - Safer Surrey Partnership - 1993

Menezes PR, Johnson S, Thornicroft G, Marshall J, Prosser D, Bebbington P, Kuipers E. Drug and alcohol problems among individuals with severe mental illnesses in south London. British Journal of Psychiatry 1996;168:612-619.

Mental Health Act - HMSO - 1983

Micheal A, Mirza S, Mirza KAH, Babu VS, Vithayathil E. Morbid jealousy in alcoholism. British Journal of Psychiatry 1995;167:668-672.

Miller WR, Rollnick S. Motivational interviewing: preparing people to change addictive behaviour. New York: Guilford Press, 1991.

Minkoff & Drake - Homelessness & Dual Diagnosis - in Treating the Homeless Mentally Ill - A Report of the Task Force on the Homeless mentally Ill. American Psychiatric Association

Mullaney JA, Trippett CJ. Alcohol dependence and phobias: clinical description and relevance. British Journal of Psychiatry 1979;135:565-573.

Multi-Agency Collaboration with MDOs in Surrey - University of Brighton 1994

Murphy GE. Suicide in alcoholism. New York: Oxford University Press, 1992.

Newman R, Miller N. Substance abuse and psychosis. Current Opinion in Psychiatry 1992;5(3):25-28.

OPCS - Survey of Psychiatric Morbidity in GB - Bulletin 1 1994 OPCS

OPCS - Report 3 - Economic Activity and Social Functioning of Adults with Psychiatric Disorders 1995 OPCS

Osher & Kofoed - Treatment of Patients with Psychiatric & Psychoactive Substance Abuse Disorders - Hospital & Community Psychiatry Oct 1989 Vol 40 No 10

Penick et al. - The Emerging Concept of Dual Diagnosis - An Overview & Implication. Haworth Press 1990

Polcin D. - Issues in the Treatment of Dual Diagnosis Clients who have Chronic Mental Illness - Professional Psychology Research & Practice. 1992 Vol 23 No 1

Prins H. - Keeping the "Mad" out of Prisons - The Magistrate p.114-5 - July / August 1994

Pristach CA, Smith CM. Medication compliance and substance abuse among schizophrenic patients. Hospital and Community Psychiatry 199o;41:1345-1348.

Reed Report - A Review of Health andSocial Services for Mentally Disordered Offenders and Others Requiring Similar Services - HMSO - 1992

Regier DA, Farmer ME, Rae DS, Locke BZ, Keith SJ, Judd LL, Goodwin FK. Comorbidity of mental disorders with alcohol and other drug abuse. Journal of the American Medical Association 1990;264:2511-2518.

Renshaw J. (ed) - Mental health and Drinking Problems: Conference Papers - Alcohol Concern / Good Practices in Mental Health - 1989

Report of the Inquiry into the Circumstances Leading to the Death of Jonathan Newby - July 1995 -HMSO

Rich CL, Fowler RC, Fogarty LA, Young D. San Diego suicide study: III relationships between diagnosis and stressors. Archives of General Psychiatry 1988;45:589-592.

Russell J. Ed - Alcohol and Crime - Mental Health Foundation - 1993

Schuckit MA, Monteiro MG. Alcoholism, anxiety and depression. British Journal of Addiction 1988;83:1373-1380.

Selzer JA, Lieberman JA. Schizophrenia and substance abuse. Psychiatric Clinics of North America 1993;16:401-412.

Smith J, Hucker S. Schizophrenia and substance abuse. British Journal of Psychiatry 1994;165:13-21.

A Strategy for Mentally Disordered Offenders in Surrey - November 1994 - Standing C'tee on MDO's.

Sudbury PR, Ghodse AH. - Solvent misuse - Current Opinion in Psychiatry 1990;3:388-392.

Tackling Drugs Together - HMSO - 1995

Volpicelli JR, Watson NT, King AC, Sherman CE, O'Brien CP - Effect of naltrexone on alcohol "high" in alcoholics - American Journal of Psychiatry 1995;152:613-615.

Weller M. et al. - Drug Abuse and Mental Illness - Lancet 30 April 1988 p. 997.

Winston A, Laikin M, Pollack J, Samstag LW, McCullough L, Muran JC. Short-term psychotherapy of personality disorders. American Journal of Psychiatry 1994;151:190-194.

Wolk-Wasserman D. - Contacts of suicidal alcohol and drug abuse patients and their significant others with public care institutions before the suicide attempt - Acta Psychiatrica Scandinavica - 1987;76:394-405.

OTHER PUBLICATIONS FROM WYNNE HOWARD BOOKS

ALCOHOL PROBLEMS IN OLD AGE

Mike Ward & Chris Goodman
(1995 80pages A5)
This is a practical and easy to read guide to working with this difficult client group. It provides an introduction to the nature of alcohol problems among older people; how to identify them; advice on sensible drinking limits for older people; and practical guidance on encouraging clients to change; as well as tools to be used with older problem drinkers and pointers to working with clients who are reluctant to change their drinking
Code BB001 £5.95uk / $9usa
Postage £0.70p uk / $3usa
£2.00 other parts of world

WHO KNOWS BEST? Developing User Involvement In Substance Misuse Services

Surrey Alcohol & Drug Service Users' Forum (1995 A4 32pages)
This booklet outlines the process undertaken in Surrey to generate service user involvement in the alcohol and drugs field. It is not a guide on "how to get it right", but rather an honest description of the struggles undergone and the innovative solutions developed.
code BB002 £4.95uk / $8usa
Postage £0.70p uk / $3usa
£2.00 other parts of world

THE BLACK BOTTLE

George Cruickshank
(1847 Size 5" x 3" 16pages)
Sixteen engraved illustrations from the nineteenth century temperance movement, tracing the decline and fall of a respectable family under the influence of drink. A fascinating source of interesting illustrations for OHP trans-parencics, training handouts and reports.
Code BB006 £1.00uk / $1.50usa
Postage £0.35p uk / $1usa
£0.70p other parts of world

ALCOHOL ISSUES IN CHILD PROTECTION

Alcohol Training Project
(Size A4 spiral bound 80pages)
Few will need persuading of the importance of alcohol abuse as a key factor in child abuse. This manual offers alcohol specialists, health and social services staff, and other trainers and educators all the materials necessary to run a course on this topic.
Code BB007 £6.00uk / $10usa
Postage £0.70p uk / $3usa
£2.00 other parts of world

ALCOHOL AWARENESS... A TRANS-CULTURAL APPROACH

Alcohol Training Project
(Size A4 spiral bound 50pages)
There is growing awareness that alcohol problems are not the preserve of white European cultures. People from Afro-Caribbean and Asian communities also have such problems. This manual offers alcohol specialists, health and social services staff, and other trainers and educators all the materials necessary to run courses on this topic.
Code BB008 £6.00uk / $10usa
Postage £0.70p uk / $3usa
£2.00 other parts of world

HELPING PROBLEM DRINKERS:
A Practical Guide

Mike Ward (A4 1988 35pages)
The third edition of this popular book offers simple explanations of modern ways of working with problem drinkers. It has been made a set book on a number of alcohol counselling courses. Invaluable for primary care staff.
Code BB010 £4.00uk / $6usa
Postage £0.70p uk / $3usa
£2.00 other parts of world

THINKING ABOUT YOUR DRINKING

Mike Ward & Chris Noronha
(Size A4 1992 24pages)
This attractively produced self-help guide aims to encourage people who are concerned about their drinking to make positive changes in private.
Code BB011 £2.50uk / $4.00usa
Postage £0.70p uk / $3usa
£2.00 other parts of world

ALCOHOL SERVICES DIRECTORY 1995/96

Alcohol Concern (A5 294 pages)
Lists nearly 500 alcohol services in England and Wales - advice and coun-selling agencies, residential services, hospitals and private sector providers.
Code BB014 £15.00uk / $23usa
Postage £1.50p uk / $4usa
£2.50 other parts of world

HOW TO ORDER

Ordering is very simple. You can pay by:

1: A VISA or MASTERCARD credit card using the UK£ price in the catalogue.

2. A UK sterling or US Dollar cheque at the UK or US price in the catalogue

3. We are willing to invoice charities or public bodies such as health, social & probation services

4. Complete the form below inserting the code no. and price for each book and adding up the total price.   Use another sheet if more space is needed.

5. Add relevant postage rate.

Please send me:

___ copy/ies of_____ @ _____   subtotal_____

___ copy/ies of_____ @ _____   subtotal_____

Postage @   subtotal_____

                    GRAND TOTAL_____

___ I enclose a cheque for _____ payable to *"Wynne Howard Books"*

___ Please invoice me at the address below

___Please debit my credit card account with the sum of UK£_____

❏ VISA   ❏ MASTERCARD

Card Number|__|__|__|__|__|__|__|__|__|__|__|__|__|__|__|__|

Card Valid From_____Expiry date_____

Signature_____ Date_____

Cardholder's name address:

Name_____Address_____

_____

Tel_____Fax_____

Delivery address (if different from above):

Name_____Organisation_____

Address_____

_____

Tel_____Fax_____

Return to:Wynne Howard Publications ❏ 27 Addison Road ❏ Guildford ❏ Surrey ❏ GU1 3QQ ❏ Great Britain or fax / phone: (International code+44) -(0)1483 - 301501